To the Teacher:

The G.U.M. Drops workbooks were designed to be used as daily supplements. Each workbook is exactly 90 pages long and is roughly divided into 18 weeks. This makes the workbooks ideal to use every day for one semester. However, because the pages continually build upon each other, you can easily adapt the books to fit your schedule by doing more than one page at a time or doing a page every other day. The workbooks are written directly to the student so that they can complete the exercises unassisted. If they do require additional help, there are notes on many of the teacher pages so that you can help them work through the concepts. The number of errors is also included on the teacher pages, which you may or may not choose to share with the student in order to make the exercises easier/harder.

Contents

Complete Sentences

A complete sentence has a subject and a predicate.

The **subject** is the part of the sentence that tells *who* or *what* the sentence is about.

The **predicate** is the part of the sentence that tells *what the subject did* or *gives more information* about the subject. If there is not a subject and a predicate, it is a **fragment**.

simple simple

The red book fell off the table.

subject   predicate

The thick, dusty book.

fragment - no predicate

"The red book" is the **complete subject** in the first example. It tells who or what the sentence is about. The **simple subject** is the main noun or pronoun, "book."

The **complete predicate** is "fell off the table." It tells what happened to the subject. The **simple predicate** is the verb, "fell."

The second example is a fragment. There is a subject, but there is no predicate.

Mark any fragments. If complete, underline the complete subjects once and the complete predicates twice. Circle the simple subjects and simple predicates.

Blew warm air across the room. *fragment*

My best friend is funny.

A fuzzy rabbit hopped through the fence.

Those boys found my missing dog.

Her big green sunglasses. *fragment*

The sun peeked through the clouds.

1

Read this passage from *Kidnapped*. Make sure each underlined sentence is complete. If it is, circle the simple subject and the simple predicate. If it is not, mark the fragment as a subject (s) or a predicate (p).

My (story) (begins) in Scotland. It was early June in the year 1751. (I) (left) the house of my father for the last time. Mr. Campbell, the town minister. (s) He joined me as I passed through the gate.

"Are you sorry to leave Essendean?" he questioned me.

"Well, sir, I have been very happy here," I replied, "but as both of my parents are now gone and I have never been outside of Essendean, I don't quite know how to feel."

"Davie," Mr. Campbell said, "before your father died, he gave me a letter for you. Asked me to start you on the road to the house of Shaws." (p)

"My father was poor!" I exclaimed. "How did he know the Shaws?"

"I don't know for sure," Mr. Campbell answered, "but you share the name as well - Balfour of Shaws."

(I) finally (reached) the house of Shaws. Was very disappointed. (p) It was big, but it was dark and dreary and falling apart.

Sentence Types

There are four different types of sentences.

All sentences begin with a capital letter. However, the punctuation at the end of the sentence depends on what type of sentence it is.

Declarative sentences are statements. They end with periods.

There is a lot of snow on the ground.

Imperative sentences are commands. They also end with periods. The subject, you, is suggested but not directly stated.

understood
(you) Put your mittens on.

Interrogative sentences are questions. They end with question marks.

Do you like cold weather?

Exclamatory sentences are full of emotion. They end with exclamation points.

It's snowing!

Add capital letters and ending punctuation to the sentences below.

dad is at the grocery store

that bee stung me

what is your favorite animal

fold your clothes and put them away

betsy is drawing a picture

i scored the winning goal

Edit this passage from *Kidnapped* by adding capital letters and ending punctuation where needed. Use all three types of ending punctuation at least once.

I pounded on the door for a long time before a window opened upstairs and a man's face appeared. i told him that I had a letter to deliver, and he asked me my name.

"My name does not shame me," I replied. "I am David Balfour."

At this statement the man let me in. He asked me for the letter from Alexander, and I gasped.

I questioned, "How do you know my father's name?"

"Why wouldn't I?" he replied. "He was my brother."

I had found my uncle. Uncle Ebenezer was a very stingy man. He was not happy that I had come. his stare and actions made me uncomfortable.

The next morning I found a book, In it my father had written "To my brother Ebenezer on his fifth birthday." this puzzled me. My father must have written it when he was less than five years old himself, if he was in fact the younger brother. Were my father and uncle twins?

my uncle said no, but I could tell he was very disturbed by my question.

Review Time!

Edit this passage from *Kidnapped*. Underline any sentence fragments and mark them as subjects (s) or predicates (p).

my uncle asked me to go and get some important papers from a room at the top of a certain stairway. Climbed many stairs in the dark. Suddenly, lightning lit up the sky I could see that the stairs weren't finished. If I had not been so careful, I would have fallen from a great height Why had my uncle sent me to the tower

After carefully finding my way back down the stairs, I crept into my uncle's house. I demanded to know why he had sent me to the tower.

we were interrupted before my uncle could answer me. A cabin boy named Ransome. He had a letter from his captain for my uncle

After reading the letter, my uncle said, "All right, Davie, let's go down to Queensferry. I need to go and see Captain Hoseason, whom I do business with. after that, we'll go and see the lawyer, Mr. Rankeillor. He knew your father and can answer all of your questions."

Was still suspicious of my uncle.

Nouns

Nouns are words that name a person, place, or thing.

There are two different types of **nouns**.

Common nouns name general people, places, or things.

Proper nouns name specific people, places, or things. Proper nouns are capitalized.

	Common	Proper
Here are some examples of	sea	Mediterranean Sea
common and proper nouns.	cat	Fluffy
Notice how the common nouns	uncle	Uncle Jake
are very general and the proper	store	Clothes Warehouse
nouns are very specific.	street	Oak Street
	ship	*Little Tug*

Circle all of the nouns in the sentences below. Capitalize the proper nouns.

My aunt is going to visit. My cousin is coming as well.

I saw a cricket on the porch. I named it chirpy.

There was only one cookie left, so I gave it to sally.

My favorite state is north carolina.

Do you see that bright star?

matthew and phillip live next to applewood park.

Her favorite story is cinderella.

I think we should eat at hamburger house.

Have you ever read a book about abraham lincoln?

Read this passage from *Kidnapped*. Circle at least ten common nouns. Underline and capitalize the proper nouns.

ransome took us to the room of Captain Hoseason in Queensferry. I left my sneaky uncle to his business.

I asked the landlord of hawes inn about my uncle. I did not tell him who I was. The landlord said my uncle was not very well-liked, and many people thought he had killed Alexander Balfour.

"Why would he do that?" I asked.

"So he could have the house and lands," the landlord answered.

That's when I learned the truth. My father was the oldest son, and somehow Uncle Ebenezer had gotten his inheritance instead.

Just then Captain Hoseason and my uncle appeared. The captain whispered in my ear that I should watch out for my uncle. He also offered to take us to Mr. Rankeillor on his ship, the *covenant*. Thinking I had found a friend, I boarded the ship. When I asked why my uncle hadn't boarded, Captain Hoseason gave me a grim smile.

I ran to the railing just in time to catch a glimpse of my uncle's evil face before I was hit over the head and slipped into darkness.

Capitalization

Here are more words that are always capitalized:

days of the week	Sunday	Thursday
months of the year	April	November
holidays	St. Patrick's Day	Easter
titles of works	Charlotte's Web	Frosty the Snowman

The pronoun "I" is always capitalized even if it is not at the beginning of a sentence.

Sherry bought a shirt, but I didn't buy anything.

Here are some words that do not need to be capitalized:

seasons	autumn	summer
directions	north	east

Add capital letters where they belong in the sentences below.

my teacher said that i have to read little women this summer.

john's birthday is in september.

next tuesday i have a dentist appointment.

those birds are flying south for the winter.

when i grow up, i want to go to africa.

mom said we could watch mary poppins before we go to sleep.

last sunday we went on a picnic.

my dad has to work on labor day but not on thanksgiving.

Edit this passage from *Kidnapped*.

When i awoke, I was tied up and in pain! I was also very sick from the rolling of the sea. As I healed and got used to being on a ship, I got to know ransome and the other shipmates. Despite their roughness, many of them were kind at heart, and i enjoyed hearing their stories.

after many days on board the ship, I became the new cabin boy. It was my job to serve the officers and get them the things they needed. It wasn't hard work, but it kept me very busy.

One foggy wednesday night our ship struck another boat. There was only one survivor from the other ship, and he was brought on board the *covenant*. He was heading south to france, and he offered captain hoseason money to take him there. The captain agreed, and took the stranger to the roundhouse for some food. However, the captain was a greedy man. I heard him plotting to kill the stranger and take all of his money. The captain asked me to go to the roundhouse and get the weapons.

Review Time!

Edit this passage from *Kidnapped*.

I knew that i could not help kill a man who had done nothing wrong. Instead, I warned the man that he was in danger. He asked me if I would fight on his side, and I agreed. I was also a captive on the *covenant*, and this was my chance to be free. We had most of the weapons and a good place from which to defend ourselves. We armed ourselves and thought up a plan. We had to be ready for the enemy

I found out the man's name was alan breck stewart, He was from scotland too, but he had joined the French army. When I told him that Mr. Campbell was a good friend of mine, he was surprised. alan disliked the campbells. He warned me to stay away from a man named colin campbell, who worked for king george. colin campbell had forced many people from their homes and land in scotland over the winter and spring.

The captain and his men attacked the roundhouse! Alan and i had more weapons and a better place to fight from, and we were able to defend ourselves. They tried a second time, but we won again!

Abbreviations

Abbreviations are shorter ways to write words.

Abbreviations are used to shorten words. There are abbreviations for many proper nouns. These abbreviations are also capitalized, and they are marked with periods. Many abbreviations are simply the first few letters of the word.

There are abbreviations for the days of the week and the months of the year.

Wednesday	>	Wed.	Monday	>	Mon.
December	>	Dec.	August	>	Aug.

There are abbreviations for many "place" words, often used to name specific places.

Lake Avenue > Lake Ave.   Mount Olive > Mt. Olive

People's names sometimes have titles with them. These titles are capitalized and are often abbreviated. Initials are capitalized and marked with periods too.

President Roosevelt	>	Pres. Roosevelt
Doctor Nelsen	>	Dr. Nelsen
Misses D. Bradley	>	Mrs. D. Bradley

Add capital letters and periods where they belong in the sentences below.

on feb 4th, mr. and mrs. martin are coming to dinner

next thurs. i have to write about pres. john f kennedy

his name is dr. raymond j allen, but everyone calls him ray

my mom is taking me to a shop on robinson ave. tomorrow

11

Edit this passage from *Kidnapped*.

Capt. Hoseason had no choice but to surrender to us. We were in dangerous waters, and his best seamen had been killed. Alan did his best to help steer the ship, but the tide crashed us into a reef. I was thrown into the sea. Although I wasn't a very good swimmer, I was able to make my way to land.

I spent the next several days walking alone, but I learned that Alan was alive. He had left instructions for me to join him I asked for directions from the people I met along the road. One day I came upon a group of four men. I asked one of them for help. As we were talking, a shot rang out. The man fell from his horse. I began to chase the man who had shot him. The men thought that I had helped, and they began to chase me!

As I ran for my life, I came upon Alan, who told me to follow him. We ran as hard as we could until at last Alan felt we were safe. I learned that the man who had been shot was none other than Mr. Colin Campbell. Alan said that he had no part in the shooting.

12

Plural Nouns

Plural nouns name more than one person, place, or thing.

You can make most nouns plural just by adding **"s."**

spoon > spoon<u>s</u>   flower > flower<u>s</u>   frog > frog<u>s</u>

If a noun ends with **"ch," "sh," "s," "x," or "z,"** add **"es"** to make it plural.

ranch > ranch<u>es</u>   bush > bush<u>es</u>   glass > glass<u>es</u>

If a noun ends with **a consonant and then "y,"** change the **"y"** to **"i"** and add **"es."**

fry > fr<u>ies</u>   baby > bab<u>ies</u>   pony > pon<u>ies</u>

If a noun ends with **"f" or "fe" and makes a "v" sound in the plural**, change the **"f"** to **"v"** and end it with **"es."**

knife > kni<u>ves</u>   shelf > shel<u>ves</u>   wolf > wol<u>ves</u>

leaf > leaves

Irregular plural nouns don't follow any rules at all.

goose > geese   man > men   foot > feet

Read the nouns below. Write the plural forms in the blanks provided.

dish _dishes_   class _classes_   book _bookes_

mouse _mice_   loaf _leaves_   penny _penies_

apple _apples_   fox _foxes_   fly _flies_

13

Edit this passage from *Kidnapped*. Cross out any misspelled plural nouns and write the correct plural nouns above.

Even though Alan said he had no part in the killing of mr. [M] Campbell, I was very suspicious. However, Alan also pointed out that my only chance of escape was to run away with him. If I stayed, i [I] would be captured by the campbells [C], who thought that I had helped kill their leader. I agreed to stay with alan [A], and we shook handses [hands].

Because of the death of Colin Campbell, many soldiers came to the area. Although we had a long way to go, we had to be very careful not to be seen by the mans [men]. We ran and walked all through the night. During the day, we took turns sleeping in the bushs [bushes] and keeping watch. We went on like this for many, many days, and I got very sick. Finally, when I felt like I couldn't move my foots another step, we came to a place of safety. We rested for a couple of weeks.

As soon as i [I] was well enough to leave, we took to the road again. After just a couple of days, we were back in my part of the country This made me very happy, but we still had to be careful. The news of Colin Campbell's death had spread very fast, and we were still in danger of being caught. I had friends here, but Alan did not.

Review Time!

Edit this passage from *Kidnapped*.

Alan hid in some weeds while I went to queensferry in search of Mr. Rankeillor, the lawyer. Although at first we didn't trust each other, we shared our storys. I told the lawyer about my kidnapping, and he told me what had happened while I had been gone. Mr. Campbell had come looking for me, and my uncle had lied. He had told mr. Campbell and Mr. rankeillor that he'd given me a large sum of money and I had set off to europe for a proper education. Both persons had known my uncle was lying.

Mr. Rankeillor told me the truth about my uncle's estate. Out of all the ladys in scotland, my father and uncle had both fallen in love with the same one. In the end they had come to the agreement that my father would get the lady and my uncle would get the estate. Mr. Rankeillor also told me that i was the rightful heir of the estate. however, he warned me that my uncle would not give it up without a fight. I had a plan to catch my uncle in his lies, and Mr. Rankeillor agreed to help

Verbs

Verbs are words that show action or complete a thought.

Action verbs tell the action of the subject.

Lucy <u>opened</u> the door.   Dad <u>carved</u> the pumpkin.

The bee <u>flew</u> by me.   I <u>caught</u> the baseball.

Linking verbs link the subject to a noun, pronoun, or adjective that describes the subject. They complete a thought. They do not show action.

He <u>is</u> two years old.   Billy <u>became</u> hungry.

I <u>feel</u> sick.   They <u>are</u> late.

Helping verbs come before the main verb and help describe the action or show the time of the action.

She <u>was</u> climbing a tree.   Mom <u>had</u> planted a garden.

My friend <u>is</u> going home.   We <u>should be</u> helping Andrew.

Circle all of the verbs in the sentences below. Remember to look for action verbs, linking verbs, and helping verbs.

David (will) (ride) his bike tomorrow.

Kay and Sophia (are) busy next week.

The girls (skipped) across the yard.

The kitten (yawned) twice.

I (will) be (shopping) for two more hours.

They (look) happy.

16

Read this passage from *Kidnapped*. Mark the underlined verbs as action (a), helping (h), or linking (l) verbs.

That night I took Alan and Mr. Rankeillor to my uncle's house.
Alan <u>knocked</u> [a] on the door, and the lawyer and I hid close by.
When my uncle answered, Alan <u>told</u> [l] him that he and his friends
<u>had captured</u> [h/a] me and wanted my uncle to pay in return for my
safety. My uncle <u>replied</u> [a] that he didn't care about my safety.
Alan then asked to be paid in order to get rid of me. He
<u>mentioned</u> [l] that he knew my uncle had paid Captain Hoseason to
kidnap me. At this my uncle shared the sum he <u>had</u> [h] <u>paid</u> [a] the
captain. He said that he had paid him to sell me as a slave! After
my uncle <u>had</u> [h] <u>admitted</u> his evil act, Mr. Rankeillor and I
stepped out of the darkness. My uncle <u>was</u> very pale. He knew
that he had been caught.

I made a deal with my uncle. He <u>was</u> [h] <u>allowed</u> to live in the
house for the rest of his life, but he had to pay me two-thirds of the
estate's income.

Now that I was safely home, it was time for Alan to leave. As I
<u>was</u> [h] now a man of means, I <u>helped</u> [a] Alan return to his own
place of safety. Our adventures together <u>had</u> [h] <u>come</u> to an end.

17

Verb Tenses

Verbs tell what happened in the past, what is happening

right now, or what will happen in the future.

If a verb tells about an event that happened in the past, it is in **past tense**.

Past tense verbs often end in **-ed**.

      He <u>washed</u> the dishes.   They <u>washed</u> the dishes.

If a verb tells about an event that is happening right now, it is in **present tense**.

      He <u>washes</u> the dishes.   They <u>wash</u> the dishes.

If a verb tells about an event that is going to happen in the future, it is in **future tense**.

Future tense verbs always use the helping verb "will" or "shall."

      He <u>shall wash</u> the dishes.   They <u>will wash</u> the dishes.

Rewrite the sentences below in the tenses given.

(Past)   Laura kicked the ball.

(Present) _____ .

(Future)   They will play checkers all afternoon.

(Past) _____ .

(Present)   Dad grills hamburgers.

(Future) _____ .

18

Read this passage from *Rip Van Winkle*. Mark the underlined verbs/verb phrases as past, present, or future tense.

Anyone who <u>travels</u> *[f]* up the Hudson River is likely to notice the beautiful Kaatskill Mountains. Set on the west side of the river, the Kaatskill Mountains <u>rise</u> *[f]* up over the surrounding country. The shape and color of the mountains reflect the changes of the weather and seasons. Wives from all over the countryside claim the mountains are wonderful predictors of weather. In fair weather the mountains shine with blue and purple. At other times, the mountains are marked with a gray haze in an otherwise cloudless sky. These mountains <u>will play</u> *[f]* an important role in this story.

At the base of these wondrous mountains <u>is</u> *[p]* a small town. <u>Founded</u> *[p]* by Dutch colonists, the quaint little town is filled with yellow-brick houses. Smoke <u>rises</u> *[p]* from the chimneys on top of the shingled roofs.

Some time ago, in one of these houses (a very worn house, even at the time), there <u>lived</u> *[p]* a simple but cheerful man <u>named</u> *[p]* Rip Van Winkle.

Review Time!

Edit this passage from *Rip Van Winkle*.

Rip Van Winkle was indeed a simple and cheerful man, and he was also a very good neighbor However, rip van winkle was constantly nagged and blamed for various faults by his wife, Dame Van winkle. this daily henpecking had the effect of making Rip Van Winkle quite agreeable and long-suffering, traits which made him a favorite with the other husbands and wives in the village.

Rip Van Winkle was also very popular with the childs of the village. He made them toys, joined in their games, and told them wonderful storys.

The biggest flaw in Rip's character was his dislike of work. However, Rip would hunt or fish for hours without reward. If a neighbor asked for help with even the most difficult of tasks, rip was quick to assist. In other words, Rip Van Winkle was willing to do any work except for his own. Managing his farm and family was simply impossible for Rip Van Winkle.

Irregular Verbs

Irregular verbs do not have an -ed ending in the past tense.

While many past tense verbs end with **-ed**, there are also many that don't.

These **irregular verbs** don't follow any rules at all; they simply have to be learned.

You probably know many of them already! Here are some irregular verbs:

PRESENT		PAST	PRESENT		PAST
blow	>	blew	ride	>	rode
buy	>	bought	run	>	ran
drink	>	drank	sing	>	sang
give	>	gave	take	>	took
has	>	had	throw	>	threw
know	>	knew	wear	>	wore

Fill in each blank with the past tense of the verb given in parentheses.

Dot (see) _saw_ a firefly yesterday evening.

My father (drive) _drove_ us to our music lessons last Tuesday.

Those vases (are) _were_ sold last week.

I wanted to play tag yesterday, but instead we (swim) _swam_ .

Do you think she (write) _wrote_ me a letter?

Two weeks ago, the pastor (speak) _spoke_ about love.

Last night, two deer (run) _ran_ across the road.

The mailman (ring) _rang_ our doorbell early this morning.

Our window (break) _broke_ during the storm.

Read this passage from *Rip Van Winkle*. Cross out any incorrect irregular verbs and write the correct verbs above.

As Rip Van Winkle avoided working on his farm, it looked worse and worse after each passing year. The fences breaked down, the cow was nearly always loose, and weeds covered most of the fields.

Rip also overlooked his son and daughter, who runned about dirty and carefree. Even at his young age, Rip's son seemed to have the same idle traits as his father.

Still, Rip keeped a cheerful disposition and was happy to take life as it comed. His wife continued to nag him about his idleness, to which Rip would respond with a mere shrug. This only annoyed his wife more, who beginned her yelling and complaining all over again.

Rip Van Winkle's only true companion at home was his dog, Wolf. Also disliked by Dame Van Winkle, Wolf accompanied Rip wherever he goed.

Subject / Verb Agreement

The subject and verb in a sentence have to agree.

In present tense the verb changes form to agree with the subject. If the subject is plural, the verb must be plural. If the subject is singular, the verb must be singular. Most singular verbs end with "s."

The boys <u>chase</u> butterflies.   The boy <u>chases</u> butterflies.

Carol and Jill <u>fly</u> kites.   Carol <u>flies</u> a kite.

The singular subjects "I" and "you" do <u>not</u> follow this rule. Do not add "s" to the verb when "I" or "you" is the subject, even though they are singular.

I <u>chase</u> butterflies.   You <u>chase</u> butterflies.

I <u>fly</u> a kite.   You <u>fly</u> a kite.

Some forms of the verb "to be" change form in past and present tense. They don't follow any rules, so you will have to learn them.

He <u>is</u> sad.   I <u>am</u> sad.   You <u>are</u> sad.   They <u>are</u> sad.

Circle the correct verbs in the sentences below.

The calf and her mother (sleep / sleeps) in the sun.

The girls (sing / sings) loudly.

I (am / are) excited.

Sandra (want / wants) a drink.

He (run / runs) a mile every day.

You (plant / plants) a lot of pumpkins.

We (take / takes) flowers to our neighbor every day.

Edit this passage from *Rip Van Winkle*. Circle the correct verbs.

Time (pass / passes) slowly in some cases, and to Rip, it seemed as though it nearly crawled. As the years goed by, Rip Van Winkle growed tired of his wife's temper, which worsened with time. He often retreated to the village inn, where a crowd of wise and idle villagers gathered to gossip, share stories, and relax. The inn displayed a portrait of king george, which overlooked the gathering of villagers. Every once in a while a traveler would leave an old newspaper A lengthy discussion would follow even though the events had taken place some time ago.

This favorite retreat of Rip Van Winkle's was also taken away by his wife, who would interrupt with a severe tongue lashing for rip and the rest for their idleness. Scolding voices often (interrupt / interrupts) lazy times!

Soon Rip's only hope to escape his nagging wife (was / were) to go and hunt in the woods. Wolf went with him, and Rip Van Winkle shared his food as well as his complaints with his faithful dog. the pair enjoyed many hours of hunting away from dame Van Winkle's angry glare and harsh tongue.

24

Review Time!

Edit this passage from *Rip Van Winkle*.

One fine april day Rip and Wolf (was / were) out squirrel hunting.
They finded themselves in the highest parts of the kaatskill
mountains. Feeling tired, Rip sitted down to take a break. From his
high perch, Rip Van Winkle could admire the beautiful scenery
surrounding him. He could see the majestic hudson river silently
flowing down its lazy path far below.

On the other side Rip could see a deep, rugged mountain glen
Pieces of the surrounding cliffs fell into its depths, and the setting
sun just barely touched the wild glen. rip van winkle enjoyed the
silence and beauty of the land around him for quite some time
before getting up to leave. He sighed at the thought of the tongue
lashing he was sure to receive for arriving home so late. Dame Van
Winkle would be very angry

Pronouns

Pronouns take the place of nouns.

Sometimes nouns can be replaced by **pronouns**. Here is a list of pronouns:

I	us	me	you	he	him
her	she	it	they	them	we

An **objective pronoun** replaces a noun that is an object in a sentence.

Thad put the <u>book</u> on the table.   >   Thad put <u>it</u> on the table.

Dana gave her <u>sisters</u> a hug.   >   Dana gave <u>them</u> a hug.

The following are objective pronouns: me   you   him   her   them   it   us

A **nominative pronoun** replaces a noun that is the subject of a sentence.

<u>Thad</u> put the book on the table.   >   <u>He</u> put the book on the table.

The <u>girls</u> gave Dana a hug.   >   <u>They</u> gave Dana a hug.

The following are nominative pronouns: I   you   he   she   they   it   we

Circle the correct pronouns in the sentences below.

(He / Him) likes to go to the park. His friend goes with (he / him).

Jane has a new fish. (She / Her) named it Squirt.

Tomorrow (we / us) have to clean. Mom will help (we / us).

A new family moved in on our street. I watched (they / them).

Bill asked (I / me) if I like baseball. (I / Me) said yes.

(We / Us) went sailing. My best friend went with (we / us).

Edit this passage from *Rip Van Winkle*. Circle the correct pronouns.

Before rip had even started down the mountain, (he / him) heard someone call his name. Turning around, Rip saw only a bird Not trusting his ears, Rip decided it was just his imagination and set off once again. Just as soon as he'd taken a step, rip van Winkle heared a voice crying, "Rip Van Winkle! Rip Van Winkle!" Rip was surprised to see a figure making its way towards (he / him), carrying a heavy load upon its back. He hurried down the mountain in order to help the person with the load.

Rip was even more surprised when he got closer to the stranger. The man was very short and had lots of bushy hair to go along with his long beard. his clothes were also very odd. Although they (was / were) Dutch styles, they were from many years ago. The little man was struggling to carry a barrel of liquor up the steep mountain. (Them / It) was very heavy.

Pronoun / Antecedent Agreement

Pronouns must agree with the nouns they replace.

An **antecedent** is a word being replaced or referred to by a pronoun. The pronoun must agree in number and gender with the antecedent.

If the antecedent is singular, the pronoun must be singular.

The little <u>girl</u> was watching an ant. <u>She</u> watched for a long time.

The little girl was watching an <u>ant</u>. <u>It</u> was very busy.

If the antecedent is plural, the pronoun must be plural.

The <u>girls</u> were watching an ant. <u>They</u> watched for a long time.

The girls were watching the <u>ants</u>. The girls watched <u>them</u> work.

If the antecedent is **masculine** (referring to a boy or man), the pronoun must be masculine. If the antecedent is **feminine** (referring to a girl or woman), the pronoun must be feminine.

<u>Kevin</u> is building a tree house. <u>He</u> is almost finished.

<u>Ashley</u> has green eyes. <u>She</u> wears glasses.

Circle the correct pronouns in the sentences below.

Ben likes math. (He / They) likes word problems the most.

The birds are in a tree. (It / They) are making a nest in (it / them).

Lisa jumped into the puddle. (He / She) got her shoes wet.

The boys each had three cookies. (He / They) liked (it / them).

Mrs. Kim read a magazine. (He / She) bought (it / them) today.

28

Edit this passage from *Rip Van Winkle*. Circle the correct pronouns.

Rip van winkle felt uneasy about the stranger, but (he / him)
could see that the man could use his help. The pair continued to
climb up the mountain in a dry riverbed. They took turns carrying
the barrel. Every once in a while rip heard a loud rumble, which
he thought was a distant storm. The stranger did not talk at all
during their walk together

As they entered a hollow in the mountain, Rip was shocked to see
a whole group of strange little mans. (They / It) were all dressed
in outdated clothes, with long beards and hair. There was one thing
about the men that was odder to Rip than their appearances.
Although the men were playing a game of ninepins and seemed to
be having a party, they did not smile or laugh. Instead, they were
mysteriously quiet and serious.

The men maked signs for rip to wait on (him / them). He poured
out the liquor as quickly as they could drink it. Rip began to relax.
When no one was watching, he took a drink from the barrel. he
had one drink after another until (she / he) fell into a deep sleep.

29

Review Time!

Edit this passage from *Rip Van Winkle*.

Rip Van Winkle waked up to a sunny morning. (He / Him) had fallen asleep on the grass in the same place where he had first seen the strange man. Rip slowly remembered the events of the past night. Knowing that his wife would be angry (she / he) had stayed out all night, Rip standed up to make his way home.

Rip found a gun nearby, but instead of his nice gun he found one that was old and rusty. Suspecting he had been robbed of his weapon by the little men, Rip began to look for wolf. He called and called, but Wolf did not come. Angry, Rip decided to find the little men and his belongings.

Although rip found the riverbed he and the stranger had walked in to reach the hollow, this morning (it / they) was filled with rushing water. Rip struggled up the mountain on a different path. When he reached the place where the hollow had been, there was nothing there but solid rock

After searching for a while, Rip Van Winkle gave up and turned to go home. he (was / were) not excited about facing dame van winkle, but he had no choice but to go home empty-handed.

Possessives

Possessives show that something belongs to someone.

Most **possessive nouns** are formed by adding **apostrophe "s"** ('s).

This blanket belongs to my <u>sister</u>. It is my sister<u>'s</u> blanket.

Those boots belong to that <u>fireman</u>. They are the fireman<u>'s</u> boots.

If the possessive noun is **plural and ends with "s,"** just add an **apostrophe** (').

This house belongs to my <u>parents</u>. It is my parents<u>'</u> house.

Proper nouns can also be possessive.

The cats belong to <u>Annie</u>. They are Annie<u>'s</u> cats.

That bicycle belongs to <u>Ernie</u>. It is Ernie<u>'s</u> bicycle.

Just as pronouns replace nouns, **possessive pronouns** replace possessive nouns.

This is the <u>doctor's</u> office. This is <u>his</u> office.

That is my <u>grandparents'</u> car. That is <u>their</u> car.

Write a possessive noun or pronoun to complete each sentence below.

That store is owned by Mr. Clark. It is _____ store.

This necklace belongs to my mom. It is _____ necklace.

Those sandals belong to Lacy. They are _____ sandals.

The hamster belongs to me. It is _____ hamster.

This garden belongs to my family. It is _____ garden.

Those chips belong to the boys. They are _____ chips.

31

Read this passage from *Rip Van Winkle*. Circle as many of the possessive nouns and pronouns as you can find and add apostrophes where needed.

Rip saw many people as he entered the village, but he didn't recognize any of them. This was very strange, as Rip knew everyone in his village. Everyone stared at Rips chin. Reaching up, Rip was surprised to discover that his beard had grown a foot since he had left! Thinking the liquor had messed up his mind, Rip continued to his house.

When Rip found his house, he was shocked to see that it appeared to be abandoned. Rip hurried to the village inn, but it too was changed. In its place was an old rickety building, and instead of King Georges face there was a picture of a different man. The words identified the new face as General Washington. Confused, Rip approached the group gathered around the door.

At the sight of Rip Van Winkle, the crowd quieted. Rip scanned the crowds faces. When he didn't see anyone familiar, Rip began to question the group about his old friends. It seemed that all of Rips friends had either died or left the village a long time ago.

Contractions

A contraction is a shorter way to write two words.

Some words can be joined together to form one single word, called a **contraction**. A contraction is formed by writing the words together, taking out a letter or letters, and putting an apostrophe where the missing letters were.

were not	>	weren't	I am	>	I'm
they are	>	they're	it is	>	it's

Some common words found in contractions are pronouns and helping verbs.

you will   >   you'll   I have   >   I've

Another common word found in contractions is the adverb "not."

could not   >   couldn't   did not   >   didn't

The contraction for "will not" changes more than usual.

will not   >   won't

In the sentences below, circle the words that can be made into contractions. Write the contractions on the blanks provided.

We have been to the mountains twice.   _____

Do you think you are getting sick?   _____

Taylor was not at home yesterday.   _____

I think it is going to be warm tomorrow.   _____

Emma said she does not like snow.   _____

Edit this passage from *Rip Van Winkle*.

At this moment a woman with a baby passed by. When the baby saw Rip, it began to cry.

"Dont cry, Rip," the woman said, much to Rip Van Winkles surprise.

Rip asked the woman, "What is your name "

"Why, Im judith gardenier," she answered.

"What was your fathers name?" Rip Van Winkle questioned.

"My fathers name was Rip Van Winkle. He disappeared twenty years ago, when i was just a little girl," the woman explained.

"Im your father! I (is / am) Rip Van Winkle!" Rip cried. At last he had found someone he knew! Rip Van Winkle told his story to the villagers.

They realized that what had seemed like a single night to Rip had actually been twenty years

Rip Van Winkle moved in with his daughter and son-in-law. For the first time in his life, he was happy. Rips son was employed on his sisters farm, but he avoided his work much like his father had done. Rip Van Winkle, now an old man, had little to do but idle his time away, which suited (he / him) just fine.

Review Time!

Edit this passage from *The Secret Garden*.

Mary Lennox wasnt a very pretty child. she was extremely thin and had pale skin, light hair, and a constant frown. She had been born in india. Marys father, captain lennox, was a sickly man who worked for the English government. Her mother was very beautiful and never did anything besides go to parties. She didnt want to be bothered with a daughter, so she made her servants take care of Mary. The servants waited on Mary and gave (she / her) everything she could possibly want in order to keep her happy. Mary grew up to be very spoiled. (She / Her) didnt mean to be spoiled, but she had never had to think about anyone but herself.

When she was nine years old, Marys parents died. This was a sad thing, but it wasnt all that sad for Mary. Her parents had never spent any time with her, so Mary really hadnt known them at all. At her young, spoiled age, mary lennox simply wondered what would happen to her.

Adjectives

Adjectives are words that describe nouns and pronouns.

Adjectives tell about size, type, number, color, texture, shape, and more.

    two   big   bumpy   green   round   heavy   glass

Adjectives can also describe pronouns.   You are <u>pretty</u>.   She is <u>quiet</u>.

Here are some other types of adjectives:

<u>Articles</u> - There are three articles, "**a**," "**an**," and "**the**."

<u>Demonstrative</u> - These include words such as "**this**," "**that**," "**those**," and "**these**."

<u>Possessives</u> - Possessive nouns and pronouns function as adjectives.

<u>**Comparative** and **Superlative**</u> - These adjectives are used to compare. Comparative adjectives compare two things and often end in "**-er**." Superlative adjectives compare more than two things and often end in "**-est**."

I am young, but my sister is <u>younger</u>. Our brother is the <u>youngest</u> of all.

Irregular comparative and superlative adjectives change form completely.

    good > better > best   many > more > most

Circle all of the adjectives in the sentences below.

Her doll had big blue eyes, shiny black hair, and a button nose.

This pie is good, but those cherry tarts are better.

The long, sharp pin was hard to find in the shaggy gray carpet.

That red car is faster than Jerry's old truck.

There are several tall, strong trees in that patch of woods.

Read this passage from *The Secret Garden*. Circle as many adjectives as you can find.

As it turns out, Mary had an uncle in Yorkshire, England. His name was Mr. Archibald Craven, and he lived in a place called Misselthwaite Manor. Mary made the long trip to England. She was met by her uncle's housekeeper, Mrs. Medlock. Mrs. Medlock told Mary about her uncle and his strange house.

Mr. Craven was an odd man. He had a slight hunchback, and he traveled a lot. Misselthwaite Manor was a giant house with a hundred rooms, but many rooms were locked up and never used. It seemed like a dreary old place, and Mary was not the least bit excited about living there.

When Mary and Mrs. Medlock arrived at Misselthwaite Manor, they were met by a neat man named Mr. Pitcher. He told them that Mr. Craven didn't want to see Mary and would be leaving for London the next day. Mrs. Medlock led Mary up to her new room and told her that she was not to go wandering around the house.

Edit this passage from *The Secret Garden*.

When mary woke up the next morning, there was a young house-maid in her room. She introduced herself as Martha and began to talk to Mary. At first Mary was very cold towards martha, but soon she became interested in what (she / her) was saying. Martha had eleven brothers and sisters. One of Marthas brothers, Dickon, loved animals and knowed all about them. Mary had never been interested in another person before, but she was interested in hearing about dickon and his animal friends.

Mary had no toys here, and there were no servants to play with her. For the first time in her life, she had to entertain herself. Martha suggested that she go and play outside in the fresh, cold air. There were some very large gardens, including one that had been locked up for ten years. Martha said that it had been mrs Cravens garden. When she had died, Mr. Craven had locked it up and buried the key. After Martha left, Mary could not stop thinking about the secret garden

Edit this passage from *The Secret Garden*.

Mary went outside to explore the gardens The winter had just ended, so there wasnt all that much to look at, but it was better than being inside. She met the gardener, ben weatherstaff, and made friends with a cheerful little robin. She walked through several different walled gardens before she came to a high wall with no door. As she could see trees on the other side of the wall, she knew that it was another garden. Sure enough, it (was / were) the secret garden! Mary walked around and around the walls, but she couldnt find the door.

Each day passed like the one before for mary. She woke up, ate her breakfast, and spent most of the day outside. As Mary runned and played in the rough, fresh air, she began to get stronger. she never stopped thinking about the secret garden, and (she / her) often walked around the ivy-covered walls looking for the door.

Martha and Ben Weatherstaff warned (she / her) to stay away from the garden, but Mary found it impossible to forget about.

Edit this passage from *The Secret Garden*.

one day when Mary was walking around the secret garden yet again, the robin landed on the ground by a pile of dirt. Something caught marys eye, and she bent over to look. There was an old ring sticking out of the dirt. Mary pulled it out of the soil and found a key hanging on the ring. She hided the key in her pocket and walked around the garden again, but she still couldn't find the door.

The next afternoon mary went back to the secret garden The robin was there, and Mary couldnt help asking (them / it) to show her the door. The robin flew on top of the wall and began to sing. Just then a heavy gust of wind came. It blew the ivy away from the wall for just a moment, and Mary gasped. She had seen a doorknob underneath all of the ivy Mary pushed the ivy aside, put the key in the door, and turned the knob. She slowly pushed open the door and stepped into the secret garden.

Adverbs

Adverbs are words that describe verbs, adjectives, and other adverbs.

Adverbs are similar to adjectives. However, adjectives describe nouns and pronouns, and adverbs describe verbs, adjectives, and other adverbs. Many adverbs end in **"-ly."**

The snow is <u>not</u> falling <u>heavily</u>. (Adverbs "not" and "heavily" describing verbs)

The snow is <u>perfectly</u> white.   (Adverb "perfectly" describing adjective)

The snow is falling <u>very</u> <u>lightly</u>.   (Adverb "very" describing adverb "lightly")

Adverbs can tell when, where, how, and how much or how little.

The girl spoke <u>last</u>. (when)   The girl <u>rarely</u> spoke. (how little)

The girl spoke <u>here</u>. (where)   The girl spoke <u>quietly</u>. (how)

Comparative adverbs compare two and often end in **"-er." Superlative adverbs** compare three or more and often end in **"-est." Irregular adverbs** change completely.

I run <u>faster</u> than Paul, but Lee runs <u>fastest</u> of all.

Our team played <u>well</u>, but the other team played <u>better</u>.

Avoid using more than one negative word in the same sentence.

She did<u>n't</u> have <u>no</u> manners. > She did<u>n't</u> have <u>any</u> manners.

Circle all of the adverbs in the sentences below. Fix any double negatives.

That horse is running very quickly and is hardly sweating.

We will not get our mail today.

The girl carefully looked around and calmly crossed the street.

I never rounded no bases.

I performed poorly in the play; my sister performed better.

Read this passage from *The Secret Garden*. Circle as many adverbs as you can find.

It was extremely hard for Mary to tell if the plants in the secret garden were dead or alive. They did not look very alive, but they had just come through the cold winter. Rosebushes were scattered about on the ground, and climbing rose branches were draped carelessly on the walls and hanging around the trees. Mary carefully walked around. She noticed some tiny sprouts pushing through the grass. Mary did not know much about gardens, but she thought they could use some room. She found a sharp stick nearby and made a clearing around the sprouts.

Mary decided the garden would be her secret place. However, she did need to learn about gardening, so she asked Martha some questions. Martha generously offered to send a letter to Dickon, asking him to buy some seeds and tools for Mary. Mary could not wait to meet Dickon, and she was very excited to learn to care properly for her new garden.

Edit this passage from *The Secret Garden*.

nearly a week later Mary came upon dickon. He was sitting by a tree playing a pipe, and there were little animals all around (he / him). Mary was delighted at how he seemed to charm the furry critters. Dickon had brought Mary her supplies, and she couldnt wait to get started. she decided that Dickon was a boy she could trust, so she took him to her secret garden. Dickon loved the garden just as much as she did. (They / Them) worked in the little garden as often as they could. After breathing in the fresh, clean air and working in the garden for many days, Mary was no longer a thin, unattractive girl. She had a healthy appetite and rosy cheeks, and she often smiled.

Dickon was not the only friend that mary made. One night when Mary was in bed, she heard someone crying. Mary followed the sound through the dark house until she found the room it was coming from. She slowly pushed open the door A young boy was crying in a bed. He stopped when he saw Mary. His name was colin, and he was mr Cravens son.

Edit this passage from *The Secret Garden*.

Colin was ten years old. He was a very delicate boy with pale skin and large eyes. His father didnt like to see him because Colin reminded him of his wife. The doctors had said that colin probably wouldn't live to be very old, so everyone felt bad and gave (he / him) whatever he wanted. Since mr. craven was gone so much, Colin was the master of the house. He spent most of his time in his room, for (he / him) didn't want people to look at him or talk about him. He was very weak, and he spent all of his time sitting on the couch or lying on his bed.

Colin did enjoy talking with Mary, and he asked her to come and visit him every day He asked Mary lots of questions, and she told him all about india, dickon, and the secret garden. Because Colin was always told that he wasn't well, he always felt ill. however, Mary didn't see anything wrong with him. She treated him like he was just fine. Colin liked to spend time with Mary, for she never reminded him that he was sick.

Midterm

Edit this passage from *The Secret Garden*.

Although colin had never liked going outside, he longed to see the secret garden. A few weeks later he and Mary comed up with a plan to take him to the secret garden without anyone knowing. After the servants had brought Colin and his chair outside, he ordered (they / them) to leave him with mary

Mary and Dickon had been working in the garden for many weeks. Spring had come, and the garden was full of life again. Colin was delighted by the beautiful flowers, green grass, and cheerful birds. He looked at Mary and Dickon and exclaimed, "i am going to get well "

just as the fresh air and delightful gardening had changed Mary, it began to heal Colin. He became interested in the garden, enjoyed spending time with mary and dickon, and was determined to get well. He practiced standing and walking until he was just as strong as Dickon. However, he still pretended that he was weak and ill so that the servants didnt know he was better. Colin was waiting for his father to come home so he could surprise (he / him).

Prepositions

Prepositions add meaning to sentences by
showing time, location, or direction.

Prepositions help explain the position of objects in relation to another word in the sentence. There are many different prepositions. Here are a few common ones:

above	after	to	down	from
inside	of	over	through	up

Prepositions begin **prepositional phrases**. The prepositional phrase includes all of the words from the preposition up to a noun or pronoun, which marks the end of the prepositional phrase. This noun or pronoun is the **object of the preposition**. If there is no noun or pronoun following the preposition, the word is probably an adverb. Sometimes an adverb comes right before a preposition.

The water was flowing *underneath* the **bridge**.

adverb
I found the newspaper outside *in* the **bucket** *by* the **door**.

Underline the prepositional phrases and circle the objects of the prepositions.

We stepped up onto the ship and began our adventure at sea.

During the storm, our dog hid under my bed.

I heard footsteps outside the door.

Shelly walked to the window and looked across the lawn.

There are six ducks living over by the river.

Pete is waiting in the car.

When we went to the store, my mother had me walk beside her.

Read this passage from *The Secret Garden*. Underline all of the prepositional phrases. Circle the objects of the prepositions.

While Colin was healing in England, Mr. Craven was traveling around Europe. Mr. Craven had spent a lot of time alone in the last ten years, and he was not a very lively person. One night he had a dream about the secret garden. The next day he got a letter from home. It said that he should come home soon and that he would be glad he did.

Mr. Craven returned to Misselthwaite Manor a few days later. He felt bad that he had never spent much time with Colin.

Just as Mr. Craven was walking around the secret garden, Colin came running out of the door and accidentally ran right into his father. Mr. Craven was shocked by the sight of his son! Colin was tall and handsome and healthy! Colin led his father into the secret garden and told him how they had worked hard and brought it back to life. He also told how working in the garden had made him healthy again. Mr. Craven looked at the flowers and smiled. He decided right then that the beautiful garden would never be locked up again!

Commas

A comma marks a slight pause in a sentence.

Commas are used in many different ways.

Commas are used in large numbers with more than three digits (but not in years).

302   12,672   1,844   1,764,230

Commas are used to separate the month and day from the year in a date.

November 19, 2005   July 4, 1776   May 24, 1963

Commas are used to separate a city and state or country.

Orlando, Florida   Boston, Massachusetts   Paris, France

In letters, commas are used after the greeting and closing. The first word of the greeting and closing are capitalized.

Dear Chrissy,   Love,   Forever friends,

Aunt Fay   Nikki

Edit the letter below by adding capital letters and commas where they belong.

dear uncle robin   february 23 2007

 thank you for the wonderful birthday present. i can't believe you

mailed it all the way from wichita kansas. that is a long way!

mom says i can come in 300 days. that's over 7000 hours away!

 thanks again

        aaron

Edit this passage from *Robinson Crusoe*.

I was born in york england in 1632. My father was a merchant, and my family lived well. We (was / were) not rich, but we certainly weren't poor either. As i was the third son and not trained in any type of work, I began to think about traveling at an early age. The sea seemed to call to me, and I knew I wouldn't be happy anywhere else. When I asked my father for his permission, he would not give it to me. He said a life at sea (was / were) for men who didn't have any other choice. It was not an easy living, filled with hard work and little reward. My father told me that I would be happiest if I stayed right where I was. I could get a job and live a comfortable life just as I had always done

Although I respected my father, I could not forget about going to sea. On august 24 1650, I asked my mother to try and talk to my father. She refused because (she / her) knew he wouldnt change his mind. I found out later that she had told him anyway, and my father had replied, "That boy might be happy if he (stay / stays) here, but if he (go / goes) to sea his life will be miserable. I cannot agree to it."

Review Time!

Edit this passage from *Robinson Crusoe*.

If I had known how true my fathers words were, I would have saved myself a lot of misery. About a year later one of my friends invited me to sail to london england on one of his father's ships. I agreed without telling my parents or asking Gods blessing. The ship left on september 1 1651. I was very seasick at first, as I was not used to the rolling of the sea. Several days later our ship was caught in a terrible storm. We (was / were) rescued by some men in a smaller boat who rowed us safely to shore. When the captain heard that I had come on the voyage against my father's wishs, he told me to go back home and never venture out to sea again.

Instead of going home, I made friends with the captain of a different ship and went to sea again. the captain was a kind and honest man, and under his direction I made a small fortune. Soon afterwards the good captain died, and after a series of adventures, I came to live in the brasils.

Commas

A comma marks a slight pause in a sentence.

Commas are used to separate items in a series. This may be a series of nouns, verbs, or even whole phrases.

    My dad likes to play tennis, basketball, and soccer.

    I have to do my schoolwork, watch my sister, and fold my clothes.

Commas are used to separate two adjectives. However, no comma is needed if one or both of the adjectives is a color or number.

    The soft, fluffy bunnies were sleeping in their cage.

    The seven fluffy bunnies were sleeping in their cage.

Commas are used when people are spoken to directly.

    Please finish your milk, Katie.   Thank you, Simon, for listening.

    Children, please put your cups in the sink.

Add commas where they belong in the sentences below.

I got a bike candy and a warm fuzzy robe for Christmas.

Do you want to come with me Shane?

Red yellow and blue are all primary colors.

I need you Elizabeth to carry this bag.

That new red wagon is for you.

The large bulky box was too heavy for me to lift.

He walked jogged and ran a mile despite the hot muggy air.

Edit this passage from *Robinson Crusoe* by adding commas where they belong.

I bought as much land as I could afford and started my own sugar plantation. I had left a good part of my earlier fortune with the captain's widow, and I sent for some of it. After four years as a planter, I began to truly prosper. My plantation was another opportunity for me to settle down and enjoy a quiet comfortable life, but I was again called to the sea.

Some of my fellow planters had heard me talk about trading in Africa. They wanted me to make a trip there for them. They made me a good offer, saying, "If you go Mr. Crusoe we will take care of your plantation." I left exactly eight wonderful years after I first went to sea.

After two quiet weeks at sea, we were hit by a terrible vicious storm. Just as one of the men spotted land, the ship stuck fast in a sandbar. With the violent winds heavy rain and giant waves tearing at the ship, we feared it would be torn to pieces. We climbed into the smaller boat, but a large powerful wave flipped us all into the sea. I nearly drowned in the giant black waves, yet I alone made it to shore. I crawled up on the sand coughed the water out of my lungs and thanked God for sparing my life.

Commas

A comma marks a slight pause in a sentence.

Commas are used after an introductory word or a light exclamation at the beginning of a sentence.

No, I don't have a nickel.   Hey, the rain stopped!

Well, I'll see you later.   Wow, that snake is really long!

Commas are used after a dependent clause, long prepositional phrase, or two prepositional phrases in a row before the main part of a sentence.

Before we went to the party, I had to wrap my gift.

Just as the sun was setting, Kathy stepped outside.

Commas are used to set off an interruption in a sentence.

There was a lot to do, I was told, before we could leave.

The sandwiches were, by the way, very good.

Add commas where they belong in the sentences below.

After eating a hot lunch we went sledding.

The shoes however didn't fit.

As I watched from inside a cardinal landed on the bird feeder.

Yes my brother is older than me.

The leaves are I think very beautiful in the fall.

Oh we're going to be late!

Because it was raining we had to stay inside.

This car for example is the perfect color.

Edit this passage from *Robinson Crusoe* by adding commas where they belong.

I spent the night in a tree to keep myself safe from wild men or animals. When I woke up the storm had passed and the water was calm. The tide I was surprised to see had lifted the ship off the sandbar and grounded it again much closer to the shore. I could come within a quarter mile of the ship when the tide was out. If only we had stayed on the ship we would have survived after all! After grieving for the loss of my company I decided to go back to the ship and get anything that would be useful. On my first trip, I brought back food the carpenter's chest of tools and some weapons. When I had come safely back to land with my cargo I climbed a hill to view the land. I discovered that I was stranded on an island, with no other land to be seen besides two smaller islands off to the west. Fortunately I also discovered that there did not appear to be any dangerous creatures on this island. There were only insects birds and small animals.

Review Time!

Edit this passage from *Robinson Crusoe* by adding commas where they belong.

The ship I knew would not survive the next storm. I worked hard to get everything out that I could. Over the next thirteen days I made eleven trips to the ship. I collected many useful things, including nails hatchets cable a grindstone clothing the canvas sails a hammock bedding silverware some sheets of iron, and more food and weaponry. Then there was another long powerful storm. When it had passed, the ship was gone. I was sad, but I knew that I hadn't wasted any time and that I had in fact gotten nearly everything of value onto shore.

Well the next order of business was to find myself a place to live that would offer shelter from the sun rain and animals. It also had to be close to fresh water and offer a view of the sea in case a ship sailed close by. After searching for most of a day I found a plain on the side of a rising hill that suited my needs. There was a wall of thick black rock with a sort of hollowed-out part at the back of the plain. I pitched my tent in front of this hollow and then built a strong secure fence to protect myself and my belongings.

Commas

A comma marks a slight pause in a sentence.

Commas are used to set off an **appositive**, which is a word or phrase that renames the noun(s) or pronoun(s) right before it.

My cousins, George and Dennis, have three raccoons.

Shoe Warehouse, my favorite store, is having a sale.

Commas are used between two **complete sentences** connected by a conjunction - AND, BUT, OR, FOR, NOR, SO, or YET.

Patty was sick, <u>so</u> she stayed in bed.

This sentence is made from two complete sentences. "Patty was sick" and "she stayed in bed" are complete sentences joined by the conjunction "so."

Patty was sick <u>and</u> stayed in bed.

The second part of this sentence, "stayed in bed," is not a complete sentence, so no comma is needed.

Add commas where they belong in the sentences below.

Ask the cook the lady in the white hat for the recipe.

I wanted to knit a hat so I bought some yarn.

There were two apples but only one banana.

My dog a golden retriever loves to play outside.

I was very tired for it was after midnight.

She is going to take a bath and then a nap.

56

Edit this passage from *Robinson Crusoe* by adding commas where they belong.

It took much sweat and hard work to complete my home. Over the first several months I hollowed out a larger portion of the rock to make more room for myself and my belongings. I built a table a chair and some shelves. I also continued to strengthen my roof and fence.

During my first year on the island I looked for food regularly. There were a number of goats on the island, as well as birds and fish. I had thrown out some chicken feed in order to use the bag. A few weeks later much to my surprise I found corn and rice growing. It would be years before I could spare any for food but I was careful to gather the seed and sow it again in the proper season.

I also explored more of the island. I built a smaller home a tree fort in a pleasant valley filled with fruit trees.

I kept track of the days by cutting notches in a post. When it had been one whole year I remembered the day by fasting and setting it apart as a religious exercise. I confessed my sins prayed and praised God.

Semi-Colons

A semi-colon marks a longer pause in a sentence.

Semi-colons are similar to commas, but a semi-colon marks a longer pause.

Remember that a comma is used when two complete sentences are joined by a conjunction - AND, BUT, OR, FOR, NOR, SO, or YET. If two complete sentences are joined <u>without</u> the use of a conjunction, then a semi-colon is used.

> The boys went to the park, and they will be gone all afternoon.
>
> The boys went to the park; they will be gone all afternoon.

Another use for the semi-colon is to separate a series in which there is another series within that already uses commas.

> The farmer had cats in the barn; horses, cows, and goats in the pasture; and dogs in the yard.

Add commas and semi-colons where they belong in the sentences below.

The phone rang it was my aunt.

Macy likes to draw but she doesn't have much time.

I bought four cartons of yogurt now there are only three.

We liked that roller coaster it was exciting.

Robert can come inside or stay in the car.

I ordered water to quench my thirst a burger french fries and cole slaw for my meal and a chocolate milkshake for dessert.

58

Edit this passage from *Robinson Crusoe* by adding commas and semi-colons where they belong.

Over the next several years I kept myself busy with many different tasks. I went hunting and fishing I made baskets candles dishes and clothes and I cleared land for farming. I planted my corn and rice each year until I finally had enough to spare some for eating. Then I had to figure out how to grind it up and bake it into bread. These things would have been simple with the proper tools and knowledge but in my case they took a very long time.

I also explored the whole of the island. I captured a parrot and taught it to speak found turtles to add to my diet and succeeded in taming a goat. I continued to harvest fruit and dry grapes for I enjoyed having raisins with my bread when it was too wet to go out and hunt.

After eleven years on the island I decided to capture some goats and tame them so that I wouldn't have to hunt. I built a pen and captured a few young goats within three and a half years I had a nice flock. Now I had a good supply of meat and milk and after many attempts I was also able to make butter and cheese.

Review Time!

Edit this passage from *Robinson Crusoe* by adding commas and semi-colons where they belong.

In my fifteenth year on the island I made a startling discovery. I found a man's footprint in the sand it was much too big to be my own. I was so shaken that I ran to my fortress and didn't come out for three days. My mind raced with wild thoughts and I pondered what I should do. I had planted trees so thick around my fence that it was completely hidden but I planted more to add extra security.

I lived in fear for two years without seeing any other sign of human life. Then one day I came upon the remains of a bonfire. I could see that these were cannibals who had come from one of the smaller islands. After making this unsettling discovery I stayed close to my home for two more years.

Some years later I saw five large canoes land on my shore. They were filled with cannibals. One of their prisoners tried to escape. Three of the cannibals chased him but I scared them away with my weapons. The prisoner was very surprised to see me but very grateful for my help. I named him Friday this was the day I had saved him. Friday the escaped prisoner came to live with me.

Quotes

A quote is the exact words of a speaker.

A **quote** is something someone says directly. It is only a quote if it is the exact words of the speaker. Quotes are marked with **quotation marks**.

"I like fish," Rhonda said. "They are so colorful!"
This is a quote. Rhonda is speaking.

Rhonda said that she likes fish because they are so colorful.
This is not a quote. Rhonda is not speaking. Someone else is telling us what Rhonda said. It does not need quotation marks.

Read the sample quote near the top of the page. Notice that quotation marks come in pairs - they mark both ends of the quote and are outside of the punctuation.
"Rhonda said" is not inside the quotations because it is not part of what she said.

Add quotation marks where they belong in the sentences below.

Monica asked, Where do the stars hide during the day?

My neighbor told me he was going on vacation.

I don't like storms, the little girl stated. They are very scary!

Callie said that she doesn't like peas.

I made apple pie, Mom said. It will be ready in an hour.

Here is your newspaper, the boy said.

My uncle replied, You're welcome.

Edit this passage from *Robinson Crusoe*.

As friday was himself a cannibal, I was very careful at first.
However I soon found that I had nothing to worry about. Although
he couldnt speak English, he took great care to let (I / me) know
that he was my servant. I soon learned to trust Friday he became
my faithful companion. I taught him English and showed him all
that I had accomplished on the island. I fed him goat and made
him understand that he was never to eat a human again. I also
taught him how to use a gun, which he was very scared of at first.
Friday and i lived together for three years. These were the
happiest years I spent on the island.

In my twenty-seventh year on the island the cannibals came back
again. Friday and I were able to rescue two of their prisoners. One
of them was a Spaniard and the other one was Fridays father!
Both of the men were thankful for our help and willingly placed
themselves under my leadership.

Now that you (is / are) here father, Friday said, I am truly
content.

Quotes

A quote is the exact words of a speaker.

The first word of a quote is always capitalized even if it does not start the sentence. If the quote is split in the middle of a sentence, as in the second example below, still capitalize only the first word of the quote. The quotation marks are placed at each end of the quote, but they don't include the name of the speaker or the word "said."

Dad said, "My vegetables are growing well."

"The tomatoes," Dad said, "are starting to turn red."

"The beans are nearly ready," Dad said. "Soon we'll eat them."

Unless the quote is separated from the speaker by an exclamation point or question mark, there is a comma separating the quote from the speaker. All punctuation goes inside the quotation marks.

"When will you be home?" I asked.

I asked, "Will you be gone long?"

"I will see you soon," he said.

Add capital letters and punctuation to the sentences below.

look at that alligator bruce said it has sharp teeth

why are we whispering I whispered

run my sister yelled

my favorite tree mom said is the mighty oak

shannon said this is my house

the boy said that he wasn't hungry

63

Edit this passage from *Robinson Crusoe*.

Several months later I saw an English ship. Since there hadn't been any storms, I was suspicious that these men were up to no good. Eleven of the men came on shore in a boat and three of them were bound. These three were left under a tree while the others left to explore the island.

Come along Friday I ordered. We are going to investigate

We armed ourselves and went to speak with the bound men. One of them was the captain of the ship one was his mate and the other was a passenger.

The captain explained the rest of the soldiers have mutinied. They are going to leave us here and take the ship

I freed the three men after they had pledged their loyalty to me. The captain and I came up with a plan to take his ship back. We attacked the men who had betrayed the captain and spared those the captain knew were good men. We left the leaders of the mutiny on the island the rest of us set sail. After twenty-eight years on the island, I was finally on my way home!

Review Time!

Edit this passage from *Little Women*.

It isn't going to feel like Christmas without any presents, Jo complained.

I hate being poor Meg joined in.

It's not fair that some girls have nothing, added Amy while other girls have lots of pretty things.

We have our family and lots of love, Beth said softly.

The other three girls cheered up a little but they were all thinking the same thing. Father was away at the war, and it didn't feel like (they / them) had their family for christmas.

The March sisters were gathered around the fire. Meg, the oldest, was sixteen. She was very pretty, with large eyes brown hair and soft white hands. Jo was fifteen years old she was nothing like her older sister. She was tall and thin, and her only true beauty was her long hair. She was not very ladylike, which often horrified her sisters. Thirteen-year-old beth was very shy and timid, and she was well-loved by everyone. The youngest Amy was twelve. She had blue eyes and golden hair and always tried her best to be a lady.

Homophones

Homophones are words that sound the same but are
spelled differently and have different meanings.

There are a lot of different homophones. You probably already know many of them.

Here are some commonly misused homophones:

are	>	We <u>are</u> hungry.	hear	>	Do you <u>hear</u> that?
our	>	This is <u>our</u> food.	here	>	It is over <u>here</u>.

it's	>	<u>It's</u> (It is) a snowman.	than	>	She has more <u>than</u> me.
its	>	<u>Its</u> nose is a carrot.	then	>	<u>Then</u> I'll go get more.

to	>	We are going <u>to</u> the lake.	there	>	<u>There</u> is a house.
too	>	They are going <u>too</u>.	their	>	It is <u>their</u> house.
two	>	There are <u>two</u> lakes.	they're	>	<u>They're</u> going inside.

Circle the correct words in the sentences below.

(To / Too / Two) of my sisters have birthdays in April.

That is (are / our) house. (It's / Its) very old. It's older (than / then) me.

The sky is very (blew / blue) today. (There / Their) are no clouds.

Have you ever (read / red) *Cinderella*? (It's / Its) a good story.

(Hear / Here) is the birds' nest. I can (hear / here) them chirping.

Lindsey likes (to / too / two) play tag. Jane likes to play (to / too / two).

The frog (ate / eight) the bug. (Than / Then) he jumped in the water.

This is my dresser. (It's / Its) drawers are very large.

Edit this passage from *Little Women*.

When mrs. march came home, the girls gathered around to (hear / here) her read a letter from Mr. March. Afterwards, the girls felt guilty for (there / their) selfish thoughts earlier in the day. Mrs. March, in her loving motherly way, reminded the girls of how they used (to / two) play Pilgrim's Progress. She told them to play it in real life and see how far they could get before their father came home.

The girls were very pleased with the idea and they each shared their burden. Megs burden was that she was too proud of her looks and didn't like to work.

Jo said my burden is being (to / too) rough and wild and always wishing I was somewhere more exciting.

Amy thought that her burden was being too selfish.

Nobody thought that good-natured beth would have a burden. However, Beth shared that her burden was envying girls with nice pianos being more timid (then / than) usual and not enjoying her housework.

The March girls were determined to rid themselves of their burdens by the time their father came home.

Edit this passage from *Little Women*.

On Christmas morning each of the girls received a beautiful Bible from their mother. The girls treasured (their / they're) precious books and decided to read them every day.

The girls had a surprise for mother as well. Instead of buying presents for themselves the girls decided to buy gifts for their mother. They bought her new gloves slippers handkerchiefs and a little bottle of perfume.

When the girls went down for breakfast, their mother had just come in from visiting a poor family. (She / He) asked the girls if they would give their Christmas breakfast away, and the girls agreed. They packed everything up and took it to the hungry hummel family, who thought the girls were Christmas angels.

The (for / four) sisters were rewarded (for / four) their kindness that evening. Mr. Laurence their rich neighbor heard about their sacrifice. He sent over all kinds of delicious treats as well as some beautiful flowers. How wonderful their christmas turned out to be after all

Edit this passage from *Little Women*.

Mr Laurence had a fifteen-year-old grandson who lived with him. His name was theodore but he preferred to be called Laurie. Jo had met Laurie once, and she had discovered that (he / him) was very lonely. Although he lived with his grandfather and many servants in a large house, he didnt have very many friends.

Jo went over to the big house one day after Mr. Laurence had left. She threw a snowball at Lauries window. He smiled and opened the window. Laurie had a cold and hadn't been out for a while. He asked Jo (to / too) come and keep him company. Mrs. March agreed to let Jo go inside.

When Jo stepped inside of the big house, she was awed by all of the beautiful things. She had brought a basket of presents from her family and Laurie was very happy. He told Jo that he often watched her family and was jealous of their love and happiness. The two became fast friends. Laurie was excited to meet the rest of the march family.

From that day on the Laurences and the Marches (was / were) very good friends. Laurie spent much of his time with the girls, who loved laurie like a brother.

Edit this passage from _Little Women_.

Although all of the girls were now free to go to Lauries house as often as they wished, it took Beth a long time to get over her shyness. Mr. Laurence owned a beautiful piano he knew that beth would love to play it. He was very kind, and he came to tell her that she could come over anytime and would not be bothered. Beth was so grateful for this wonderful gift that she decided to knit mr. Laurence a pair of slippers. Beth worked very hard on the slippers, and she was well-rewarded. Dear Mr. Laurence sent her a lovely thank-you note and a beautiful little piano

While Beth was overcoming her shyness, Amy had a trial of her own. She was often teased by the richer girls at school. One day she brought limes to pass out to her friends. Mr. Davis the teacher had outlawed limes, but Amy didnt care. Her friends had given her many limes and Amy wanted to prove that she could afford the treats (to / too). When Mr. Davis caught Amy he struck her hand and made her stand in front of the class until recess. Poor amys pride had caused her deep humiliation!

Confusing Words

Some words are often confused with similar words.

Here are some tips to help you remember which word to use when:

a - Use "a" before a consonant sound.   > I saw <u>a</u> baby elephant.

an - Use "an" before a vowel sound.   > I saw <u>an</u> elephant.

can - Use "can" to say that you are able.   > I <u>can</u> swim.

may - Use "may" to ask permission.   > <u>May</u> I go swimming?

good - "Good" is an adjective. Use it with nouns. > This is a <u>good</u> song.

well - "Well" is an adverb. Use it with verbs.   > She sings <u>well</u>.

lie - "Lie" means to rest or recline. > I am going to <u>lie</u> on my bed.

lay - "Lay" means to put or place.   > I will <u>lay</u> my clothes on my bed.

Circle the correct words in the sentences below.

That was a very (good / well) meal. (Can / May) I be excused?

She is going to (lie / lay) down. She has (a / an) headache.

I (can / may) bake cupcakes. I bake very (good / well).

There is (a / an) ostrich. It has (a / an) large egg.

This is a really (good / well) book. It ended (good / well).

(Can / May) we go to the beach? I will bring (a / an) picnic lunch.

Please (lie / lay) the newspaper on the table.

Edit this passage from *Little Women*.

Jo's character was also tested. She and Amy had (a / an) fight, and Jo said she would never forgive Amy. One day Jo went ice skating with Laurie. Amy followed them but Jo refused to wait for her younger sister. As a result of Jo's impatience Amy was (to / too) far away to (here / hear) that the ice was thin in the middle. She falled into the cold water below. Jo and Laurie rescued her; Jo begged for forgiveness. The (to / two) sisters were friends again!

Meg did not escape without learning a lesson of her own. When Meg was invited for a stay with her friend, Annie Moffat, she was very excited. annie moffat was very rich and dressed very (good / well). Meg couldn't help comparing her old dressis to Annies new ones. One night Meg let the other girls dress her up for a party. They fixed her hair loaned her a dress and made her look like a doll. Meg enjoyed all of the pretty things until she saw Laurie, who disapproved of her outfit. Meg was ashamed that she had let her pride take over her (good / well) sense.

Edit this passage from *Little Women*.

One day Laurie saw the March sisters walking out of their house. the four girls stopped in a shady clearing and began to work. Meg was sewing Amy was sketching and jo was knitting and reading out loud. Beth was gathering pinecones for decorations. Laurie asked if (he / him) could join them, and Meg said that he was welcome as long as he wasnt idle. This was one of the ways the girls played Pilgrim's Progress. When they had nothing else to do, they came to the clearing to enjoy the outdoors but still keep busy.

As the group enjoyed their work, they began to talk about their dreams. Laurie said that his was to travel and become a famous musician. Meg wanted to be the mistress of a lovely house filled with beautiful things. Jo wanted a stable full of horses and (a / an) inkstand that was magic to help her write wonderful stories. Now that Beth had her wonderful piano, she wanted nothing more than to stay at home with Mother and Father. Amy wanted to go to rome and become the goodest artist in the world.

Edit this passage from *Little Women*.

Jo spent much of her time busily writing by herself, trying to perfect her storys.

One day she threw her pen down with a sigh and exclaimed This is the best I can do! If (its / it's) not (good / well) enough, I'll just have to wait!

Jo packed up her papers and quietly left the house. She walked to a building in town, where she stayed for less (then / than) ten minutes.

For the next two weeks, Jos sisters thought she acted very strangely. It was plain to see she had a secret but no one knew what it was. One day Jo came inside with a newspaper. She read a story out loud to her sisters. They all enjoyed it and Beth asked who had written it. Jo showed them the paper. her name was printed underneath the story! Her dreams (was / were) starting to come true

Edit this passage from *Little Women*.

One dreary day in november, the March family received a telegram.
Mrs. March read it and dropped onto her chair. Jo took the
telegram and read (it / them) to the others. It said that (they're /
their) father was very sick! Mrs March made plans to take the train
to see him the very next morning, and the girls flyed about helping
her get ready.

Mrs. March did not have the money for the long journey. She
would have to borrow it from old aunt march. Jo feeling helpless
suddenly ran out of the house. When she came back, she handed
her mother twenty-five dollars.

Where did you get this Mrs. March asked.

Jo pulled off her bonnet, and the family gasped at her short curly
hair. Jo had sold her long brown locks!

mrs. march was very grateful. She left early the next morning,
telling the girls to hope and keep busy.

Prefixes and Suffixes

A prefix is a group of letters that can be added to the beginning of a word.

A suffix is a group of letters that can be added to the end of a word.

Here are some common prefixes and their meanings:

fore - before in time   >   I heard the weather <u>fore</u>cast for tomorrow.

    >   The author <u>fore</u>shadowed the ending.

non - not   >   The statement wasn't true; it was <u>non</u>sense.

    >   Science textbooks are <u>non</u>fiction.

re - back, again   >   I need to <u>re</u>turn these scissors to my mom.

    >   My teacher told me to <u>re</u>write my essay.

Here are some common suffixes and their meanings:

able - can be   >   Brian is a very lov<u>able</u> boy.

    >   That glass vase is break<u>able</u>.

ess - female   >   Molly was our wait<u>ress</u>.

    >   The lion<u>ess</u> was resting in the shade.

ing - an action   >   The boys were runn<u>ing</u> to the swings.

  or process   >   My dad enjoys golf<u>ing</u>.

Try to guess the meanings of the following prefixes and suffixes.

I was <u>un</u>happy because the decision was <u>un</u>just.   _____

The <u>tri</u>cycle had a <u>tri</u>angular seat.   _____

My mother was thank<u>ful</u> that I was so help<u>ful</u>.   _____

Dennis wav<u>ed</u> and call<u>ed</u> out a friendly greeting.   _____

Edit this passage from *Little Women*.

For the first week their mother was gone, the March girls behaved very (good / well). However, they soon slipped back into more carefree ways. Only Beth remembered her mother's instructions. She faithfully visited the poor Hummels every day. One day beth came home crying, and Jo went to comfort her. Beth had just come back from the hummel's house. The baby had been sick, and it had died on Beths lap while Mrs Hummel was getting the doctor. when the doctor had arrived, he said it had died of scarlet fever. Meg and Jo had already had scarlet fever but Amy and Beth had not.

Beth did get the fever, and Amy was sent away to live with aunt March until Beth was better. Beth was very sick for many days, sicker (then / than) her sisters ever knew. Meg and Jo were relieved when their mother came home. They had done their best to nurse Beth, but (they / them) were very weary of the heavy burden. Just when it seemed that Beth could get no worse she beginned to get better. She was finally able to sit on the couch and play with her kittens or sew again.

Edit this passage from *Little Women*.

Although Beth never really got her strength back, she was soon more like her old self. Amy returned home and the household (was / were) cheerful once again. Mr. March was also doing much better he wrote that he would be able to come home soon.

During these peaceful weeks, christmas came again. The girls enjoyed their thoughtful gifts from each other Mrs. March and old Mr. Laurence. Just when the girls decided they couldnt hold any more happiness, Laurie burst in the door with another surprise. Mr. March walked in behind him, and the girls began laughing and crying. Everyone gathered close by while mr. march told the story of his travels.

The happy family sat down to Christmas dinner. Mr. March could see the differences in his little women after their dedication to Pilgrim's Progress. He speaked to his daughters kindly, complimenting each one on her improved virtues. Despite their lack of money, the March family felt very rich indeed

Edit this passage from *The Call of the Wild*.

Buck was four years old when man struck gold in the Klondike. Because Buck was a dog he was unaware that this event would greatly change his life. Buck had lived his whole life at judge miller's place in Santa Clara Valley california. Judge Miller owned a big house with a large porch. Behind the house were stables servants' cottages pastures and orchards. This was the wondrous home over which Buck ruled.

He went swimming and hunting with Judge Miller's sons, and he accompanied Judge Millers daughters on their frequent walks. On cold nights Buck enjoyed resting at Judge Miller's feet by the warm fire.

Buck's father was a St. Bernard, and his mother was a Scotch shepherd dog. Buck was not as big as his father but he was nevertheless a handsome dog of 140 pounds. Although buck enjoyed an easy life, his love of hunting and other outdoor activities had shaped his muscles and kept him from being a spoiled house dog.

Edit this passage from *The Call of the Wild*.

As Buck continued to enjoy his (good / well) life at Judge Miller's house, (their / there) were two things he did not know. The first was the gold strike in the Klondike. The second was that Manuel one of the gardeners was not someone Buck should have trusted.

Manuel was very good at wasting his money. Instead of using his money to take care of his family he gambled it away.

One night manuel took Buck for a walk. Only one other person saw them, and that person gave Manuel some money. Manuel put a rope around Bucks neck and handed the rope to the stranger. Buck had learned to trust men but he didnt trust the stranger. He growled at the man, who pulled the rope tighter. Buck was shocked He had never been treated harshly before.

Buck was loaded on a train and passed from stranger to stranger. Several days later Buck arrived in seattle caged in a crate.

Expressive Words

Expressive words make writing more exciting.

You can make a good story even better by using **expressive words**. When you write nouns, try and make them exact. When you use a verb or adverb, choose one that is powerful. When you use adjectives to describe something, use ones that are flavorful.

Read the pairs of sentences below. The first sentence in each pair is boring. The second sentence is the same basic sentence rewritten with exact nouns, powerful verbs and adverbs, and flavorful adjectives. They are much more lively!

The garden had lots of flowers.

The colorful garden was overflowing with beautiful daffodils.

The bear caught a fish in the water.

The large grizzly scooped a rainbow trout out of the sparkling river.

Rewrite the sentences using expressive nouns, verbs, adverbs, and adjectives.

The girl ran across the street.

_____

We had a party for Tracy.

_____

He drew a picture.

_____

I had a glass of water.

_____

Edit this passage from *The Call of the Wild*.

In Seattle Buck learned another harsh lesson. He learned that he must obey a man with a weapon. During Buck's time here he saw many other dogs come and go. Men would come and give the man in charge money, and (then / than) they would take some dogs. buck wondered where the dogs went, and he knowed one day he would find out.

Sure enough, one day a man named Perrault gave the man some money and took Buck and Curly, a Newfoundland, away with him. They joined another man named francois. Buck soon learned that Perrault and Francois worked for the Canadian government. They were fair mans, and Buck learned to respect them.

Perrault and Francois also had two other dogs. The first dog Dave took no interest in anything and seemed almost bored. The other dog, spitz, seemed friendly, but he was sneaky and cared only about himself. He often tried to steal food from the other dogs.

Edit this passage from *The Call of the Wild*.

When Buck and his new owners landed in dyea alaska, Buck saw snow for the very first time. At first it startled him, and Francois and Perrault laughed at him. However the snow was not the only new thing there.

Buck soon learned the rules of wild dogs. Here the dogs were not friends every dog had to take care of himself. Although in his old life Buck never would have stolen, here he learned to steal food from his owners and from the other dogs.

Francois and Perrault buyed several more dogs. Soon they were ready to get to work. As couriers for the Canadian government, the men were in charge of delivering important dispatches. They needed a team of strong hardy dogs to pull their sled many miles through the cold and snow

Although Buck had never worked as a sled dog he learned very quickly. Spitz was a (good / well) lead dog, but Francois and Perrault were even more impressed by buck.

Edit this passage from *The Call of the Wild*.

As Buck and the team runned day after day, Buck grew used to the work. His muscles strengthened his feet hardened and he learned to live in the cold weather. The dogs were pushed very hard they were exhausted by the end of each day.

One day Spitz attacked Buck. Spitz always a bully was jealous of the attention Buck received. Francois separated Buck from Spitz, but from that moment on they were enemys. At the end of another long day Spitz stole Bucks sleeping spot.

As the leader of the team, spitz (was / were) responsible for keeping the other dogs in line. Buck began to rebel, and he encouraged the other dogs to cause trouble as well.

Finally the time came. Spitz stole a rabbit that Buck had chased down and Buck refused to walk away. This time the dogs were going to fight it out, and only the winner would come back.

Edit this passage from *The Call of the Wild.*

The next morning francois and perrault were surprised to see that Spitz was gone. They chose a new dog to be the leader, but Buck would not let them harness the new dog up. Instead Buck insisted on being the lead dog. He felt like he had earned it. Finally Francois and Perrault gived in and made Buck the new leader.

Buck wasted no time. He made the other dogs pull and run as fast as (they / them) could. With Buck in the lead Francois and Perrault made record time.

Official orders forced Francois and Perrault to sell the dogs, which made the men very unhappy. Now the dogs pulled a heavy load of mail for some other men Even though the team was making good time, (there / their / they're) was so much mail that the dogs werent able to get enough rest between runs. Eventually these men (to / too) were ordered to sell the tired dogs.

buck and the rest of the exhausted team (was / were) bought for a very low price by an inexperienced family joining the search for gold.

Sentence Combining

Sometimes it is helpful to combine two or more short sentences into one longer sentence.

Instead of using several short, choppy sentences, sometimes two or more thoughts can be combined into one sentence.

> We went on a hike. We hiked through the woods. I saw a deer and two raccoons. I also saw a lot of birds.

These four sentences can easily be combined into a single sentence.

> I saw a deer, two raccoons, and lots of birds on our hike through the woods.

Combine each group of sentences below into one sentence.

I'm going to the potluck. I'm taking lasagna. I'm also taking a salad.

I bought a card for my mom. It was a Mother's Day card. The card was pink and white.

Our dog had puppies. They are cute. There are five of them.

Arthur is good at math. He is good at science. He likes spelling the most.

I have to wash the dishes. I also need to dust the shelves. After that I have to sweep the floor.

Edit this passage from *The Call of the Wild*.

The team was bought by a man named charles. He was traveling with his wife, mercedes, and his brother-in-law, hal. As soon as Buck walked into his new owners' camp, he knew that he and the other dogs were not going to get the rest they needed. The family was hoping to strike it rich but they were not prepared for the hard journey. Their camp was a complete mess they had brought way too many things with them.

Charles Mercedes and Hal did not know very much about dogs either. When Buck and his team were unable to pull the overloaded sled Hal decided that the dogs were just being lazy. He refused to lighten their load, even though many other people warned him that it was (to / too) heavy for the dogs to move.

Finally the family was forced to leave some of their belongings behind and buy more dogs

Edit this passage from *The Call of the Wild*.

Even with a lighter sled and more dogs, life was hard for buck and his team. They had still not gotten the chance to rest after their long mail days and their new owners did not know how to care for them properly.

Life on the trail was much harder than charles and his family had anticipated. They did not adapt very well. They were not able to cover as many miles each day as they had planned, and the family began to run out of supplies. The dogs were given less food each day but (they / them) were still expected to work just as hard.

Other people along the long dangerous trail often tried to give Charles and Hal advice, but they were too proud to listen.

One day Buck could not get up. Despite a beating from Hal, he was unable to move. A man named john thornton stopped Hal and rescued Buck. As Charles and Hal and the other dogs disappeared from sight, John knelt next to Buck and speaked to him kindly. Buck was going to get the rest he needed at last.

Edit this passage from *The Call of the Wild*.

Buck enjoyed a wonderful life with John Thornton. he was able to relax and let his body fully recover from the hard work of the past months.

Although Buck had shared a deep friendship with judge miller and his family, he had never loved anyone as he grew to love John Thornton. John treated his dogs as though they were his children and he and Buck became closer and closer. Buck did not care about the rest of mankind after his hard life, but he refused to leave John.

One day some men were bragging about how much weight (their / they're) dogs could pull. John Thornton stated that Buck could pull a sled weighing 1000 pounds. The other men did not believe him, and a bet was made.

Buck was harnessed to the sled the excitement began to build.

John knelt down and whispered As you love me Buck.

Buck strained and pulled and succeeded in pulling the sled 100 yards

Another man offered a lot of money for buck, but John Thornton refused to sell him.

Final Examination

Edit this passage from *The Call of the Wild*.

Although at first Buck could hardly stand to leave John Thorntons side he could not resist the call of the wild. Sometimes he would leave the camp to run among the trees, searching for something he didnt understand.

One night (he / him) met up with a wolf and Buck was filled with a wild excitement as they ran through the woods together. However Buck remembered John, and he couldn't bear to leave him. Buck returned to the camp but he would often leave to run wild in the woods.

Buck left the camp for longer and longer periods of time, until once he was gone for several days When he returned to the camp he found john thornton and his partners dead, killed by the arrows of Indians.

With his last tie to mankind broken, buck answered the call of the wild. He joined the pack of wolves and runned about the woods, carefree and wild. Buck ran at the head of the pack, joyfully singing the song of the wolfs.

Complete Sentences

If your students need additional help understanding complete sentences, write more examples of sentences and ask them to point out the subject and the predicate in each one. Ask them leading questions such as "Who or what is this sentence about?" "What happened to the subject or what information did we learn about it?"

Students may find it easier to work through the exercise by reading each sentence out loud and asking themselves the same questions.

Mark any fragments. If complete, underline the complete subjects once and the complete predicates twice. Circle the simple subjects and simple predicates.

Blew warm air across the room. (fragment)

My best friend is funny.

A fuzzy rabbit hopped through the fence.

Those boys found my missing dog.

Her big green sunglasses. (fragment)

The sun peeked through the clouds.

1

Read this passage from *Kidnapped*. Make sure each underlined sentence is complete. If it is, circle the simple subject and the simple predicate. If it is not, mark the fragment as a subject (s) or a predicate (p).

My story begins in Scotland. It was early June in the year 1751. I left the house of my father for the last time. Mr. Campbell, the town minister. (s) He joined me as I passed through the gate.

"Are you sorry to leave Essendean?" he questioned me.

"Well, sir, I have been very happy here," I replied, "but as both of my parents are now gone and I have never been outside of Essendean, I don't quite know how to feel."

"Davie," Mr. Campbell said, "before your father died, he gave me a letter for you. Asked me to start you on the road to the house of Shaws." (p)

"My father was poor!" I exclaimed. "How did he know the Shaws?"

"I don't know for sure," Mr. Campbell answered, "but you share the name as well - Balfour of Shaws."

I finally reached the house of Shaws. Was very disappointed. (p) It was big, but it was dark and dreary and falling apart.

2

Sentence Types

It is sometimes possible to end a sentence more than one way. The most common confusion is whether to use a period or an exclamation point. In certain instances either one can be used with only a slight change in meaning. For this reason, it is not "wrong" if students use periods in place of exclamation points or vice versa, unless the sentence obviously requires one or the other. If this ever happens, simply take the opportunity to discuss both possibilities and decide which would be more effective.

Add capital letters and ending punctuation to the sentences below.

Dad is at the grocery store.

That bee stung me!

What is your favorite animal?

Fold your clothes and put them away.

Betsy is drawing a picture.

I scored the winning goal!

3

Edit this passage from *Kidnapped* by adding capital letters and ending punctuation where needed. Use all three types of ending punctuation at least once.

There are 9 errors in this passage.

I pounded on the door for a long time before a window opened upstairs and a man's face appeared. I told him that I had a letter to deliver, and he asked me my name.

"My name does not shame me," I replied. "I am David Balfour."

At this statement the man let me in. He asked me for the letter from Alexander, and I gasped.

I questioned, "How do you know my father's name?"

"Why wouldn't I?" he replied. "He was my brother."

I had found my uncle! Uncle Ebenezer was a very stingy man. He was not happy that I had come. His stare and actions made me uncomfortable.

The next morning I found a book. In it my father had written "To my brother Ebenezer on his fifth birthday." This puzzled me. My father must have written it when he was less than five years old himself, if he was in fact the younger brother. Were my father and uncle twins?

My uncle said no, but I could tell he was very disturbed by my question.

4

91

Review Time!

Edit this passage from *Kidnapped*. Underline any sentence fragments and mark them as subjects (s) or predicates (p).

There are 10 errors in this passage.

<u>M</u>y uncle asked me to go and get some important papers from a room at the top of a certain stairway. <u>Climbed many stairs in the dark.</u> (p) Suddenly, lightning lit up the sky<u>!</u> I could see that the stairs weren't finished. If I had not been so careful, I would have fallen from a great height<u>!</u> Why had my uncle sent me to the tower<u>?</u>

After carefully finding my way back down the stairs, I crept into my uncle's house. I demanded to know why he had sent me to the tower.

<u>W</u>e were interrupted before my uncle could answer me. <u>A cabin boy named Ransome.</u>(s) He had a letter from his captain for my uncle<u>.</u>

After reading the letter, my uncle said, "All right, Davie, let's go down to Queensferry. I need to go and see Captain Hoseason, whom I do business with. <u>A</u>fter that, we'll go and see the lawyer, Mr. Rankeillor. He knew your father and can answer all of your questions."

<u>Was still suspicious of my uncle.</u> (p)

5

Nouns

If students need more help with nouns, think of nouns together until the students are able to easily think of them on their own. Try changing some of the nouns into proper nouns until they understand the difference.

Help students understand that sometimes words like "Mom" and "Dad" may take the place of a name. For example, in the sentence "<u>Mom</u> planted some flowers," *Mom* is capitalized because it is used in place of a name - "<u>Julie</u> planted some flowers." However, in the sentence "<u>My mom</u> planted some flowers," it is not capitalized because you would not put a name there - "<u>My Julie</u> planted some flowers."

Titles used with names are capitalized - "<u>Uncle Jake.</u>"

Circle all of the nouns in the sentences below. Capitalize the proper nouns.

My aunt is going to visit. My cousin is coming as well.

I saw a cricket on the porch. I named it <u>C</u>hirpy.

There was only one cookie left, so I gave it to <u>S</u>ally.

My favorite state is <u>N</u>orth <u>C</u>arolina.

Do you see that bright star?

<u>M</u>atthew and <u>P</u>hillip live next to <u>A</u>pplewood <u>P</u>ark.

Her favorite story is <u>C</u>inderella.

I think we should eat at <u>H</u>amburger <u>H</u>ouse.

Have you ever read a book about <u>A</u>braham <u>L</u>incoln?

6

Read this passage from *Kidnapped*. Circle at least ten common nouns. Underline and capitalize the proper nouns.

<u>Ransome</u> took us to the room of <u>Captain Hoseason</u> in <u>Queensferry</u>. I left my sneaky uncle to his business.

I asked the landlord of <u>Hawes Inn</u> about my uncle. I did not tell him who I was. The landlord said my uncle was not very well-liked, and many people thought he had killed <u>Alexander Balfour</u>.

"Why would he do that?" I asked.

"So he could have the house and lands," the landlord answered.

That's when I learned the truth. My father was the oldest son, and somehow <u>Uncle Ebenezer</u> had gotten his inheritance instead.

Just then <u>Captain Hoseason</u> and my uncle appeared. The captain whispered in my ear that I should watch out for my uncle. He also offered to take us to <u>Mr. Rankeillor</u> on his ship, the *Covenant*. Thinking I had found a friend, I boarded the ship. When I asked why my uncle hadn't boarded, <u>Captain Hoseason</u> gave me a grim smile.

I ran to the railing just in time to catch a glimpse of my uncle's evil face before I was hit over the head and slipped into darkness.

7

Capitalization

Point out to students that small, unimportant words like "the," "a," and "of" in titles are not usually capitalized unless they are the first word of the title.

Add capital letters where they belong in the sentences below.

<u>M</u>y teacher said that <u>I</u> have to read <u>L</u>ittle <u>W</u>omen this summer.

<u>J</u>ohn's birthday is in <u>S</u>eptember.

<u>N</u>ext <u>T</u>uesday <u>I</u> have a dentist appointment.

<u>T</u>hose birds are flying south for the winter.

<u>W</u>hen <u>I</u> grow up, <u>I</u> want to go to <u>A</u>frica.

<u>M</u>om said we could watch <u>M</u>ary <u>P</u>oppins before we go to sleep.

<u>L</u>ast <u>S</u>unday we went on a picnic.

<u>M</u>y dad has to work on <u>L</u>abor <u>D</u>ay but not on <u>T</u>hanksgiving.

8

Edit this passage from *Kidnapped*.

There are 11 errors in this passage.

    When I awoke, I was tied up and in pain. I was also very sick from the rolling of the sea. As I healed and got used to being on a ship, I got to know Ransome and the other shipmates. Despite their roughness, many of them were kind at heart, and I enjoyed hearing their stories.

    After many days on board the ship, I became the new cabin boy. It was my job to serve the officers and get them the things they needed. It wasn't hard work, but it kept me very busy.

    One foggy Wednesday night our ship struck another boat. There was only one survivor from the other ship, and he was brought on board the *Covenant*. He was heading south to France, and he offered Captain Hoseason money to take him there. The captain agreed and took the stranger to the roundhouse for some food. However, the captain was a greedy man. I heard him plotting to kill the stranger and take all of his money! The captain asked me to go to the roundhouse and get the weapons.

9

Edit this passage from *Kidnapped*.

There are 18 errors in this passage.

    I knew that I could not help kill a man who had done nothing wrong. Instead, I warned the man that he was in danger. He asked me if I would fight on his side, and I agreed. I was also a captive on the *Covenant*, and this was my chance to be free. We had most of the weapons and a good place from which to defend ourselves. We armed ourselves and thought up a plan. We had to be ready for the enemy!

    I found out the man's name was Alan Breck Stewart. He was from Scotland too, but he had joined the French army. When I told him that Mr. Campbell was a good friend of mine, he was surprised. Alan disliked the Campbells. He warned me to stay away from a man named Colin Campbell, who worked for King George. Colin Campbell had forced many people from their homes and land in Scotland over the winter and spring.

    The captain and his men attacked the roundhouse! Alan and I had more weapons and a better place to fight from, and we were able to defend ourselves. They tried a second time, but we won again!

10

Abbreviations

  While some abbreviations do not begin with capital letters and end with periods (such as those for units of measure), all of those covered in this book do. Students simply need to watch for abbreviations in the passages they edit and make sure they are capitalized and marked with periods.

Add capital letters and periods where they belong in the sentences below.

On Feb. 4th, Mr. and Mrs. Martin are coming to dinner.
Next Thurs. I have to write about Pres. John F. Kennedy.
His name is Dr. Raymond J. Allen, but everyone calls him Ray.
My mom is taking me to a shop on Robinson Ave. tomorrow.

11

Edit this passage from *Kidnapped*.

There are 12 errors in this passage.

    Capt. Hoseason had no choice but to surrender to us. We were in dangerous waters, and his best seamen had been killed. Alan did his best to help steer the ship, but the tide crashed us into a reef. I was thrown into the sea. Although I wasn't a very good swimmer, I was able to make my way to land.

    I spent the next several days walking alone, but I learned that Alan was alive. He had left instructions for me to join him. I asked for directions from the people I met along the road. One day I came upon a group of four men. I asked one of them for help. As we were talking, a shot rang out. The man fell from his horse. I began to chase the man who had shot him. The men thought that I had helped, and they began to chase me!

    As I ran for my life, I came upon Alan, who told me to follow him. We ran as hard as we could until at last Alan felt we were safe. I learned that the man who had been shot was none other than Mr. Colin Campbell. Alan said that he had no part in the shooting.

12

93

Plural Nouns

If students need more examples, make a list of plural nouns for each group ("sh," "y," "f," etc.). Have students try to think of several on their own, particularly for irregular plural nouns.

Read the nouns below. Write the plural forms in the blanks provided.

dish ___dishes___   class ___classes___   book ___books___

mouse ___mice___   loaf ___loaves___   penny ___pennies___

apple ___apples___   fox ___foxes___   fly ___flies___

Edit this passage from *Kidnapped*. Cross out any misspelled plural nouns and write the correct plural nouns above.

There are 11 errors in this passage.

Even though Alan said he had no part in the killing of Mr. Campbell, I was very suspicious. However, Alan also pointed out that my only chance of escape was to run away with him. If I stayed, I would be captured by the Campbells, who thought that I had helped kill their leader. I agreed to stay with Alan, and we shook [hands].

Because of the death of Colin Campbell, many soldiers came to the area. Although we had a long way to go, we had to be very careful not to be seen by the [men]. We ran and walked all through the night. During the day, we took turns sleeping in the [bushes] and keeping watch. We went on like this for many, many days, and I got very sick. Finally, when I felt like I couldn't move my [feet] another step, we came to a place of safety. We rested for a couple of weeks.

As soon as I was well enough to leave, we took to the road again. After just a couple of days, we were back in my part of the country. This made me very happy, but we still had to be careful. The news of Colin Campbell's death had spread very fast, and we were still in danger of being caught. I had friends here, but Alan did not.

Review Time!

Edit this passage from *Kidnapped*.

There are 13 errors in this passage.

Alan hid in some weeds while I went to Queensferry in search of Mr. Rankeillor, the lawyer. Although at first we didn't trust each other, we shared our [stories]. I told the lawyer about my kidnapping, and he told me what had happened while I had been gone. Mr. Campbell had come looking for me, and my uncle had lied. He had told Mr. Campbell and Mr. Rankeillor that he'd given me a large sum of money and I had set off to Europe for a proper education. Both [people] had known my uncle was lying.

Mr. Rankeillor told me the truth about my uncle's estate. Out of all the [ladies] in Scotland, my father and uncle had both fallen in love with the same one. In the end they had come to the agreement that my father would get the lady and my uncle would get the estate. Mr. Rankeillor also told me that I was the rightful heir of the estate. However, he warned me that my uncle would not give it up without a fight. I had a plan to catch my uncle in his lies, and Mr. Rankeillor agreed to help.

Verbs

If students need some extra practice with verbs, encourage them to come up with several verbs of each type. To make it easier, you could write sentences with blanks for verbs and then let the students fill them in.

On the other hand, if the exercise seems easy for students, you may want to go an extra step and have them identify each verb in the exercise as an action, linking, or helping verb.

Circle all of the verbs in the sentences below. Remember to look for action verbs, linking verbs, and helping verbs.

David will ride his bike tomorrow. (helping, action)

Kay and Sophia are busy next week. (linking)

The girls skipped across the yard. (action)

The kitten yawned twice. (action)

I will be shopping for two more hours. (helping, helping, action)

They look happy. (linking)

Read this passage from *Kidnapped*. Mark the underlined verbs as action (a), helping (h), or linking (l) verbs.

That night I took Alan and Mr. Rankeillor to my uncle's house. Alan knocked(a) on the door, and the lawyer and I hid close by. When my uncle answered, Alan told(a) him that he and his friends had(h) captured(a) me and wanted my uncle to pay in return for my safety. My uncle replied(a) that he didn't care about my safety. Alan then asked to be paid in order to get rid of me. He mentioned(a) that he knew my uncle had paid Captain Hoseason to kidnap me. At this my uncle shared the sum he had(h) paid(a) the captain. He said that he had paid him to sell me as a slave! After my uncle had(h) admitted(a) his evil act, Mr. Rankeillor and I stepped out of the darkness. My uncle was(l) very pale. He knew that he had been caught.

I made a deal with my uncle. He was(h) allowed(a) to live in the house for the rest of his life, but he had to pay me two-thirds of the estate's income.

Now that I was safely home, it was time for Alan to leave. As I was(l) now a man of means, I helped(a) Alan return to his own place of safety. Our adventures together had(h) come(a) to an end.

17

Verb Tenses

If your students need additional help with verb tenses, try an exercise where they change verbs into different tenses. For example, use the framework "Today she _____ ; yesterday she _____ ; tomorrow she _____ ." Then pick a simple verb like "talk" and have students fill in the blanks. "Today she talks; yesterday she talked; tomorrow she will talk." Let them practice with several different verbs before they move on to the exercise.

Rewrite the sentences below in the tenses given.

(Past)   Laura kicked the ball.
(Present) Laura kicks the ball   .
(Future)   They will play checkers all afternoon.
(Past)   They played checkers all afternoon   .
(Present)   Dad grills hamburgers.
(Future) Dad will/shall grill hamburgers   .

18

Read this passage from *Rip Van Winkle*. Mark the underlined verbs/verb phrases as past, present, or future tense.

Anyone who travels (present) up the Hudson River is likely to notice the beautiful Kaatskill Mountains. Set on the west side of the river, the Kaatskill Mountains rise (present) up over the surrounding country. The shape and color of the mountains reflect the changes of the weather and seasons. Wives from all over the countryside claim the mountains are wonderful predictors of weather. In fair weather the mountains shine with blue and purple. At other times, the mountains are marked with a gray haze in an otherwise cloudless sky. These mountains will play (future) an important role in this story.

At the base of these wondrous mountains is (present) a small town. Founded (past) by Dutch colonists, the quaint little town is filled with yellow-brick houses. Smoke rises (present) from the chimneys on top of the shingled roofs.

Some time ago, in one of these houses (a very worn house, even at the time), there lived (past) a simple but cheerful man named (past) Rip Van Winkle.

19

Review Time!

Edit this passage from *Rip Van Winkle*.

There are 10 errors in this passage

Rip Van Winkle was indeed a simple and cheerful man, and he was also a very good neighbor. However, Rip Van Winkle was constantly nagged and blamed for various faults by his wife, Dame Van Winkle. This daily henpecking had the effect of making Rip Van Winkle quite agreeable and long-suffering, traits which made him a favorite with the other husbands and wives in the village.

Rip Van Winkle was also very popular with the [children] of the village. He made them toys, joined in their games, and told them wonderful [stories].

The biggest flaw in Rip's character was his dislike of work. However, Rip would hunt or fish for hours without reward. If a neighbor asked for help with even the most difficult of tasks, Rip was quick to assist. In other words, Rip Van Winkle was willing to do any work except for his own. Managing his farm and family was simply impossible for Rip Van Winkle!

20

95

Irregular Verbs

Students probably know and use most irregular verbs already. However, some of them might be a little tricky. To familiarize students with irregular verbs, use the same framework you used when introducing verb tense. For example, with the irregular verb "eat," students would say "Today they eat; yesterday they ate."

Fill in each blank with the past tense of the verb given in parentheses.

Dot (see)__saw__ a firefly yesterday evening.

My father (drive)__drove__ us to our music lessons last Tuesday.

Those vases (are)__were__ sold last week.

I wanted to play tag yesterday, but instead we (swim)__swam__ .

Do you think she (write)__wrote__ me a letter?

Two weeks ago, the pastor (speak)__spoke__ about love.

Last night, two deer (run)__ran__ across the road.

The mailman (ring)__rang__ our doorbell early this morning.

Our window (break)__broke__ during the storm.

21

Read this passage from *Rip Van Winkle*. Cross out any incorrect irregular verbs and write the correct verbs above.

There are 6 incorrect irregular verbs in this passage.

As Rip Van Winkle avoided working on his farm, it looked worse and worse after each passing year. The fences [broke] down, the cow was nearly always loose, and weeds covered most of the fields.

Rip also overlooked his son and daughter, who [ran] about dirty and carefree. Even at his young age, Rip's son seemed to have the same idle traits as his father.

Still, Rip [kept] a cheerful disposition and was happy to take life as it [came]. His wife continued to nag him about his idleness, to which Rip would respond with a mere shrug. This only annoyed his wife more, who [began] her yelling and complaining all over again.

Rip Van Winkle's only true companion at home was his dog, Wolf. Also disliked by Dame Van Winkle, Wolf accompanied Rip wherever he [went].

22

Subject / Verb Agreement

It may help students to read the sentences out loud.

Circle the correct verbs in the sentences below.

The calf and her mother (sleep / sleeps) in the sun.

The girls (sing / sings) loudly.

I (am / are) excited.

Sandra (want / wants) a drink.

He (run / runs) a mile every day.

You (plant / plants) a lot of pumpkins.

We (take / takes) flowers to our neighbor every day.

23

Edit this passage from *Rip Van Winkle*. Circle the correct verbs.

There are 8 errors in this passage.

Time (pass / passes) slowly in some cases, and to Rip, it seemed as though it nearly crawled. As the years [went] by, Rip Van Winkle [grew] tired of his wife's temper, which worsened with time. He often retreated to the village inn, where a crowd of wise and idle villagers gathered to gossip, share stories, and relax. The inn displayed a portrait of King George, which overlooked the gathering of villagers. Every once in a while a traveler would leave an old newspaper. A lengthy discussion would follow even though the events had taken place some time ago.

This favorite retreat of Rip Van Winkle's was also taken away by his wife, who would interrupt with a severe tongue lashing for Rip and the rest for their idleness. Scolding voices often (interrupt / interrupts) lazy times!

Soon Rip's only hope to escape his nagging wife (was / were) to go and hunt in the woods. Wolf went with him, and Rip Van Winkle shared his food as well as his complaints with his faithful dog. The pair enjoyed many hours of hunting away from Dame Van Winkle's angry glare and harsh tongue.

24

Review Time!

Edit this passage from *Rip Van Winkle.*

There are 12 errors in this passage.

One fine April day Rip and Wolf (was / were) out squirrel hunting. They [found] themselves in the highest parts of the Kaatskill Mountains. Feeling tired, Rip [sat] down to take a break. From his high perch, Rip Van Winkle could admire the beautiful scenery surrounding him. He could see the majestic Hudson River silently flowing down its lazy path far below.

On the other side Rip could see a deep, rugged mountain glen. Pieces of the surrounding cliffs fell into its depths, and the setting sun just barely touched the wild glen. Rip Van Winkle enjoyed the silence and beauty of the land around him for quite some time before getting up to leave. He sighed at the thought of the tongue lashing he was sure to receive for arriving home so late. Dame Van Winkle would be very angry!

25

Pronouns

Circle the correct pronouns in the sentences below.
(He / Him) likes to go to the park. His friend goes with (he / him).
Jane has a new fish. (She / Her) named it Squirt.
Tomorrow (we / us) have to clean. Mom will help (we / us).
A new family moved in on our street. I watched (they / them).
Bill asked (I / me) if I like baseball. (I / Me) said yes.
(We / Us) went sailing. My best friend went with (we / us).

26

Edit this passage from *Rip Van Winkle*. Circle the correct pronouns.

There are 6 errors in this passage.

Before Rip had even started down the mountain, (he / him) heard someone call his name. Turning around, Rip saw only a bird. Not trusting his ears, Rip decided it was just his imagination and set off once again. Just as soon as he'd taken a step, Rip Van Winkle [heard] a voice crying, "Rip Van Winkle! Rip Van Winkle!" Rip was surprised to see a figure making its way towards (he / him), carrying a heavy load upon its back. He hurried down the mountain in order to help the person with the load.

Rip was even more surprised when he got closer to the stranger. The man was very short and had lots of bushy hair to go along with his long beard. His clothes were also very odd. Although they (was / were) Dutch styles, they were from many years ago. The little man was struggling to carry a barrel of liquor up the steep mountain. (Them / It) was very heavy.

27

Pronoun / Antecedent Agreement

Circle the correct pronouns in the sentences below.
Ben likes math. (He / They) likes word problems the most.
The birds are in a tree. (It / They) are making a nest in (it / them).
Lisa jumped into the puddle. (He / She) got her shoes wet.
The boys each had three cookies. (He / They) liked (it / them).
Mrs. Kim read a magazine. (He / She) bought (it / them) today.

28

97

Edit this passage from *Rip Van Winkle*. Circle the correct pronouns.

There are 8 errors in this passage.

Rip Van Winkle felt uneasy about the stranger, but (he / him) could see that the man could use his help. The pair continued to climb up the mountain in a dry riverbed. They took turns carrying the barrel. Every once in a while Rip heard a loud rumble, which he thought was a distant storm. The stranger did not talk at all during their walk together.

As they entered a hollow in the mountain, Rip was shocked to see a whole group of strange little [men]. (They / It) were all dressed in outdated clothes, with long beards and hair. There was one thing about the men that was odder to Rip than their appearances. Although the men were playing a game of ninepins and seemed to be having a party, they did not smile or laugh. Instead, they were mysteriously quiet and serious.

The men [made] signs for Rip to wait on (him / them). He poured out the liquor as quickly as they could drink it. Rip began to relax. When no one was watching, he took a drink from the barrel. He had one drink after another until (she / he) fell into a deep sleep.

29

Edit this passage from *Rip Van Winkle*.

There are 9 errors in this passage.

Rip Van Winkle [woke] up to a sunny morning. (He / Him) had fallen asleep on the grass in the same place where he had first seen the strange man. Rip slowly remembered the events of the past night. Knowing that his wife would be angry (she / he) had stayed out all night, Rip [stood] up to make his way home.

Rip found a gun nearby, but instead of his nice gun he found one that was old and rusty. Suspecting he had been robbed of his weapon by the little men, Rip began to look for Wolf. He called and called, but Wolf did not come. Angry, Rip decided to find the little men and his belongings.

Although Rip found the riverbed he and the stranger had walked in to reach the hollow, this morning (it / they) was filled with rushing water. Rip struggled up the mountain on a different path. When he reached the place where the hollow had been, there was nothing there but solid rock!

After searching for a while, Rip Van Winkle gave up and turned to go home. He (was / were) not excited about facing Dame Van Winkle, but he had no choice but to go home empty-handed.

30

Possessives

Possessives ending with "s" can be tricky. If a singular noun ends with an "s" or a "z" sound, you may just add an apostrophe. However, there is one exception. If a singular noun ending with "s" is a one-syllable word, it requires both an apostrophe and "s."

For example: **Bess's favorite colors are blue and purple.**

Write a possessive noun or pronoun to complete each sentence below.
That store is owned by Mr. Clark. It is _Mr. Clark's , his_ store.
This necklace belongs to my mom. It is _my mom's , her_ necklace.
Those sandals belong to Lacy. They are _Lacy's , her_ sandals.
The hamster belongs to me. It is ___my___ hamster.
This garden belongs to my family. It is _my family's , our_ garden.
Those chips belong to the boys. They are _the boys' , their_ chips.

31

Read this passage from *Rip Van Winkle*. Circle as many of the possessive nouns and pronouns as you can find and add apostrophes where needed.

Rip saw many people as he entered the village, but he didn't recognize any of them. This was very strange, as Rip knew everyone in his village. Everyone stared at Rip's chin. Reaching up, Rip was surprised to discover that his beard had grown a foot since he had left! Thinking the liquor had messed up his mind, Rip continued to his house.

When Rip found his house, he was shocked to see that it appeared to be abandoned. Rip hurried to the village inn, but it too was changed. In its place was an old rickety building, and instead of King George's face there was a picture of a different man. The words identified the new face as General Washington. Confused, Rip approached the group gathered around the door.

At the sight of Rip Van Winkle, the crowd quieted. Rip scanned the crowd's faces. When he didn't see anyone familiar, Rip began to question the group about his old friends. It seemed that all of Rip's friends had either died or left the village a long time ago.

32

98

Contractions

If students have trouble with the exercise, have them look over the page again at the common words found in contractions (pronouns, helping verbs, and "not."). Then they can look for these words in the sentences.

In the sentences below, circle the words that can be made into contractions. Write the contractions on the blanks provided.

We have been to the mountains twice. _____We've_____

Do you think you are getting sick? _____you're_____

Taylor was not at home yesterday. _____wasn't_____

I think it is going to be warm tomorrow. _____it's_____

Emma said she does not like snow. _____doesn't_____

Edit this passage from *Rip Van Winkle*.

There are 13 errors in this passage.

At this moment a woman with a baby passed by. When the baby saw Rip, it began to cry.

"Don't cry, Rip," the woman said, much to Rip Van Winkle's surprise.

Rip asked the woman, "What is your name?"

"Why, I'm Judith Gardenier," she answered.

"What was your father's name?" Rip Van Winkle questioned.

"My father's name was Rip Van Winkle. He disappeared twenty years ago, when I was just a little girl," the woman explained.

"I'm your father! I (is / am) Rip Van Winkle!" Rip cried. At last he had found someone he knew! Rip Van Winkle told his story to the villagers.

They realized that what had seemed like a single night to Rip had actually been twenty years!

Rip Van Winkle moved in with his daughter and son-in-law. For the first time in his life, he was happy. Rip's son was employed on his sister's farm, but he avoided his work much like his father had done. Rip Van Winkle, now an old man, had little to do but idle his time away, which suited (he / him) just fine.

Review Time!

Edit this passage from *The Secret Garden*.

There are 13 errors in this passage.

Mary Lennox wasn't a very pretty child. She was extremely thin and had pale skin, light hair, and a constant frown. She had been born in India. Mary's father, Captain Lennox, was a sickly man who worked for the English government. Her mother was very beautiful and never did anything besides go to parties. She didn't want to be bothered with a daughter, so she made her servants take care of Mary. The servants waited on Mary and gave (she / her) every-thing she could possibly want in order to keep her happy. Mary grew up to be very spoiled. (She / Her) didn't mean to be spoiled, but she had never had to think about anyone but herself.

When she was nine years old, Mary's parents died. This was a sad thing, but it wasn't all that sad for Mary. Her parents had never spent any time with her, so Mary really hadn't known them at all. At her young, spoiled age, Mary Lennox simply wondered what would happen to her.

Adjectives

You may wish to point out to students that adjectives can come before or after the word they modify.

Circle all of the adjectives in the sentences below.

Her doll had big blue eyes, shiny black hair, and a button nose.

This pie is good, but those cherry tarts are better.

The long, sharp pin was hard to find in the shaggy gray carpet.

That red car is faster than Jerry's old truck.

There are several tall, strong trees in that patch of woods.

Read this passage from *The Secret Garden*. Circle as many adjectives as you can find.

As it turns out, Mary had an uncle in Yorkshire, England. His name was Mr. Archibald Craven, and he lived in a place called Misselthwaite Manor. Mary made the long trip to England. She was met by her uncle's housekeeper, Mrs. Medlock. Mrs. Medlock told Mary about her uncle and his strange house.

Mr. Craven was an odd man. He had a slight hunchback, and he traveled a lot. Misselthwaite Manor was a giant house with a hundred rooms, but many rooms were locked up and never used. It seemed like a dreary old place, and Mary was not the least bit excited about living there.

When Mary and Mrs. Medlock arrived at Misselthwaite Manor, they were met by a neat man named Mr. Pitcher. He told them that Mr. Craven didn't want to see Mary and would be leaving for London the next day. Mrs. Medlock led Mary up to her new room and told her that she was not to go wandering around the house.

37

Edit this passage from *The Secret Garden*.

There are 9 errors in this passage.

When Mary woke up the next morning, there was a young house-maid in her room. She introduced herself as Martha and began to talk to Mary. At first Mary was very cold towards Martha, but soon she became interested in what (she / her) was saying. Martha had eleven brothers and sisters. One of Martha's brothers, Dickon, loved animals and [knew] all about them. Mary had never been interested in another person before, but she was interested in hearing about Dickon and his animal friends.

Mary had no toys here, and there were no servants to play with her. For the first time in her life, she had to entertain herself. Martha suggested that she go and play outside in the fresh, cold air. There were some very large gardens, including one that had been locked up for ten years. Martha said that it had been Mrs. Craven's garden. When she had died, Mr. Craven had locked it up and buried the key. After Martha left, Mary could not stop thinking about the secret garden.

38

Edit this passage from *The Secret Garden*.

There are 8 errors in this passage.

Mary went outside to explore the gardens. The winter had just ended, so there wasn't all that much to look at, but it was better than being inside. She met the gardener, Ben Weatherstaff, and made friends with a cheerful little robin. She walked through several different walled gardens before she came to a high wall with no door. As she could see trees on the other side of the wall, she knew that it was another garden. Sure enough, it (was / were) the secret garden! Mary walked around and around the walls, but she couldn't find the door.

Each day passed like the one before for Mary. She woke up, ate her breakfast, and spent most of the day outside. As Mary [ran] and played in the rough, fresh air, she began to get stronger. She never stopped thinking about the secret garden, and (she / her) often walked around the ivy-covered walls looking for the door.

Martha and Ben Weatherstaff warned (she / her) to stay away from the garden, but Mary found it impossible to forget about.

39

Edit this passage from *The Secret Garden*.

There are 8 errors in this passage.

One day when Mary was walking around the secret garden yet again, the robin landed on the ground by a pile of dirt. Something caught Mary's eye, and she bent over to look. There was an old ring sticking out of the dirt. Mary pulled it out of the soil and found a key hanging on the ring. She [hid] the key in her pocket and walked around the garden again, but she still couldn't find the door.

The next afternoon Mary went back to the secret garden. The robin was there, and Mary couldn't help asking (them / it) to show her the door. The robin flew on top of the wall and began to sing. Just then a heavy gust of wind came. It blew the ivy away from the wall for just a moment, and Mary gasped. She had seen a doorknob underneath all of the ivy! Mary pushed the ivy aside, put the key in the door, and turned the knob. She slowly pushed open the door and stepped into the secret garden.

40

Adverbs

Some words can function as adverbs or prepositions. If it is an adverb, it will not be followed by a noun or a pronoun. For example, in the third sentence of the exercise, "around" is an adverb because it is not followed by a noun or pronoun. However, if the sentence said "The girl carefully looked **around** the corner," "around" would be a preposition as it is followed by the noun "corner." Adverbs often come right before prepositions, as in the sentence, "The girl looked **around** inside the car." Students should understand this before trying to find the adverbs on the next page (42). They will get more practice and direction on the prepositions page (46).

It is important that students understand that "not" is an adverb because it is very common and is often buried in a contraction.

Circle all of the adverbs in the sentences below. Fix any double negatives.

That horse is running very quickly and is hardly sweating.
We will not get our mail today.
The girl carefully looked around and calmly crossed the street.
I never rounded no bases. I never rounded any bases.
I performed poorly in the play; my sister performed better.

41

Read this passage from *The Secret Garden*. Circle as many adverbs as you can find.

It was extremely hard for Mary to tell if the plants in the secret garden were dead or alive. They did not look very alive, but they had just come through the cold winter. Rosebushes were scattered about on the ground, and climbing rose branches were draped carelessly on the walls and hanging around the trees. Mary carefully walked around. She noticed some tiny sprouts pushing through the grass. Mary did not know much about gardens, but she thought they could use some room. She found a sharp stick nearby and made a clearing around the sprouts.

Mary decided the garden would be her secret place. However, she did need to learn about gardening, so she asked Martha some questions. Martha generously offered to send a letter to Dickon, asking him to buy some seeds and tools for Mary. Mary could not wait to meet Dickon, and she was very excited to learn to care properly for her new garden.

42

Edit this passage from *The Secret Garden*.

There are 10 errors in this passage.

Nearly a week later Mary came upon Dickon. He was sitting by a tree playing a pipe, and there were little animals all around (he / him). Mary was delighted at how he seemed to charm the furry critters. Dickon had brought Mary her supplies, and she couldn't wait to get started. She decided that Dickon was a boy she could trust, so she took him to her secret garden. Dickon loved the garden just as much as she did. (They / Them) worked in the little garden as often as they could. After breathing in the fresh, clean air and working in the garden for many days, Mary was no longer a thin, unattractive girl. She had a healthy appetite and rosy cheeks, and she often smiled.

Dickon was not the only friend that Mary made. One night when Mary was in bed, she heard someone crying. Mary followed the sound through the dark house until she found the room it was coming from. She slowly pushed open the door. A young boy was crying in a bed. He stopped when he saw Mary. His name was Colin, and he was Mr. Craven's son.

43

Edit this passage from *The Secret Garden*.

There are 9 errors in this passage.

Colin was ten years old. He was a very delicate boy with pale skin and large eyes. His father didn't like to see him because Colin reminded him of his wife. The doctors had said that Colin probably wouldn't live to be very old, so everyone felt bad and gave (he / him) whatever he wanted. Since Mr. Craven was gone so much, Colin was the master of the house. He spent most of his time in his room, for (he / him) didn't want people to look at him or talk about him. He was very weak, and he spent all of his time sitting on the couch or lying on his bed.

Colin did enjoy talking with Mary, and he asked her to come and visit him every day. He asked Mary lots of questions, and she [told] him all about India, Dickon, and the secret garden. Because Colin was always told that he wasn't well, he always felt ill. However, Mary didn't see anything wrong with him. She treated him like he was just fine. Colin liked to spend time with Mary, for she never reminded him that he was sick.

44

101

Midterm

Edit this passage from *The Secret Garden*.

There are 10 errors in this passage.

Although <u>C</u>olin had never liked going outside, he longed to see the secret garden. A few weeks later he and Mary [came] up with a plan to take him to the secret garden without anyone knowing. After the servants had brought Colin and his chair outside, he ordered (they / them) to leave him with <u>Mary.</u>

Mary and Dickon had been working in the garden for many weeks. Spring had come, and the garden was full of life again. Colin was delighted by the beautiful flowers, green grass, and cheerful birds. He looked at Mary and Dickon and exclaimed, "<u>I</u> am going to get well<u>!</u>"

<u>J</u>ust as the fresh air and delightful gardening had changed Mary, it began to heal Colin. He became interested in the garden, enjoyed spending time with <u>M</u>ary and <u>D</u>ickon, and was determined to get well. He practiced standing and walking until he was just as strong as Dickon. However, he still pretended that he was weak and ill so that the servants didn<u>'</u>t know he was better. Colin was waiting for his father to come home so he could surprise (he / him).

45

Prepositions

Students can tell the difference between an adverb and a preposition by looking for a noun or pronoun following the word. If there is a noun or pronoun, the word is a preposition. If there is not, it is probably an adverb. In the case where an adverb is right next to a preposition, help students understand that if they find two "prepositions" in a row, the first one is most likely an adverb.

Underline the prepositional phrases and circle the objects of the prepositions.

We stepped up <u>onto the ship</u> and began our adventure <u>at sea</u>.
<u>During the storm</u>, our dog hid <u>under my bed</u>.
I heard footsteps <u>outside the door</u>.
Shelly walked <u>to the window</u> and looked <u>across the lawn</u>.
There are six ducks living over <u>by the river</u>.
Pete is waiting <u>in the car</u>.
When we went <u>to the store</u>, my mother had me walk <u>beside her</u>.

46

Read this passage from *The Secret Garden*. Underline all of the prepositional phrases. Circle the objects of the prepositions.

While Colin was healing <u>in England</u>, Mr. Craven was traveling <u>around Europe</u>. Mr. Craven had spent a lot <u>of time</u> alone <u>in the last ten years</u>, and he was not a very lively person. One night he had a dream <u>about the secret garden</u>. The next day he got a letter <u>from home</u>. It said that he should come home soon and that he would be glad he did.

Mr. Craven returned <u>to Misselthwaite Manor</u> a few days later. He felt bad that he had never spent much time <u>with Colin</u>.

Just as Mr. Craven was walking <u>around the secret garden</u>, Colin came running out <u>of the door</u> and accidentally ran right <u>into his father</u>. Mr. Craven was shocked <u>by the sight</u> <u>of his son</u>! Colin was tall and handsome and healthy! Colin led his father <u>into the secret garden</u> and told him how they had worked hard and brought it back <u>to life</u>. He also told how working <u>in the garden</u> had made him healthy again. Mr. Craven looked <u>at the flowers</u> and smiled. He decided right then that the beautiful garden would never be locked up again!

47

Commas

Edit the letter below by adding capital letters and commas where they belong.

<u>D</u>ear <u>U</u>ncle <u>R</u>obin<u>,</u>   <u>F</u>ebruary 23<u>,</u> 2007

<u>T</u>hank you for the wonderful birthday present. <u>I</u> can't believe you mailed it all the way from <u>W</u>ichita<u>,</u> <u>K</u>ansas. <u>T</u>hat is a long way! <u>M</u>om says <u>I</u> can come in 300 days. <u>T</u>hat's over 7<u>,</u>000 hours away!

<u>T</u>hanks again<u>,</u>

            <u>A</u>aron

48

Edit this passage from *Robinson Crusoe*.

There are 9 errors in this passage.

  I was born in York, England in 1632. My father was a merchant, and my family lived well. We (was / were) not rich, but we certainly weren't poor either. As I was the third son and not trained in any type of work, I began to think about traveling at an early age. The sea seemed to call to me, and I knew I wouldn't be happy anywhere else. When I asked my father for his permission, he would not give it to me. He said a life at sea (was / were) for men who didn't have any other choice. It was not an easy living, filled with hard work and little reward. My father [told] me that I would be happiest if I stayed right where I was. I could get a job and live a comfortable life just as I had always done.

  Although I respected my father, I could not forget about going to sea. On August 24, 1650, I asked my mother to try and talk to my father. She refused because (she / her) knew he wouldn't change his mind. I found out later that she had told him anyway, and my father had replied, "That boy might be happy if he (stay / stays) here, but if he (go / goes) to sea his life will be miserable. I cannot agree to it."

49

Edit this passage from *Robinson Crusoe*.

There are 10 errors in this passage.

  If I had known how true my father's words were, I would have saved myself a lot of misery. About a year later one of my friends invited me to sail to London, England on one of his father's ships. I agreed without telling my parents or asking God's blessing. The ship left on September 1, 1651. I was very seasick at first, as I was not used to the rolling of the sea. Several days later our ship was caught in a terrible storm. We (was / were) rescued by some men in a smaller boat who rowed us safely to shore. When the captain heard that I had come on the voyage against my father's [wishes], he told me to go back home and never venture out to sea again.

  Instead of going home, I made friends with the captain of a different ship and went to sea again. The captain was a kind and honest man, and under his direction I made a small fortune. Soon afterwards the good captain died, and after a series of adventures, I came to live in the Brasils.

50

Commas

  For the first rule, using commas in a series, students are taught to use commas after each item. However, students may notice some writers omit the last comma (before "and"). This is not technically wrong, but it is becoming more and more common to use a comma here. It also helps make the sentence clearer, so it is a good habit for students to learn.

  Emphasize to students that commas are not needed if all of the words in a series are connected by the word "and."

Add commas where they belong in the sentences below.
I got a bike, candy, and a warm, fuzzy robe for Christmas.
Do you want to come with me, Shane?
Red, yellow, and blue are all primary colors.
I need you, Elizabeth, to carry this bag.
That new red wagon is for you.
The large, bulky box was too heavy for me to lift.
He walked, jogged, and ran a mile despite the hot, muggy air.

51

Edit this passage from *Robinson Crusoe* by adding commas where they belong.

There are 9 errors in this passage.

  I bought as much land as I could afford and started my own sugar plantation. I had left a good part of my earlier fortune with the captain's widow, and I sent for some of it. After four years as a planter, I began to truly prosper. My plantation was another opportunity for me to settle down and enjoy a quiet, comfortable life, but I was again called to the sea.

  Some of my fellow planters had heard me talk about trading in Africa. They wanted me to make a trip there for them. They made me a good offer, saying, "If you go, Mr. Crusoe, we will take care of your plantation." I left exactly eight wonderful years after I first went to sea.

  After two quiet weeks at sea, we were hit by a terrible, vicious storm. Just as one of the men spotted land, the ship stuck fast in a sandbar. With the violent winds, heavy rain, and giant waves tearing at the ship, we feared it would be torn to pieces. We climbed into the smaller boat, but a large, powerful wave flipped us all into the sea. I nearly drowned in the giant black waves, yet I alone made it to shore. I crawled up on the sand, coughed the water out of my lungs, and thanked God for sparing my life.

52

103

Commas

A comma may or may not be used if an introductory phrase is short, so please note that there may be times when students feel a comma is needed and it is not shown (or vice versa).

Add commas where they belong in the sentences below.
After eating a hot lunch, we went sledding.
The shoes, however, didn't fit.
As I watched from inside, a cardinal landed on the bird feeder.
Yes, my brother is older than me.
The leaves are, I think, very beautiful in the fall.
Oh, we're going to be late!
Because it was raining, we had to stay inside.
This car, for example, is the perfect color.

53

Edit this passage from *Robinson Crusoe* by adding commas where they belong.

There are 11 errors in this passage.

I spent the night in a tree to keep myself safe from wild men or animals. When I woke up, the storm had passed and the water was calm. The tide, I was surprised to see, had lifted the ship off the sandbar and grounded it again much closer to the shore. I could come within a quarter mile of the ship when the tide was out. If only we had stayed on the ship, we would have survived after all! After grieving for the loss of my company, I decided to go back to the ship and get anything that would be useful. On my first trip, I brought back food, the carpenter's chest of tools, and some weapons. When I had come safely back to land with my cargo, I climbed a hill to view the land. I discovered that I was stranded on an island, with no other land to be seen besides two smaller islands off to the west. Fortunately, I also discovered that there did not appear to be any dangerous creatures on this island. There were only insects, birds, and small animals.

54

Review Time!

Edit this passage from *Robinson Crusoe* by adding commas where they belong.

There are 20 errors in this passage.

The ship, I knew, would not survive the next storm. I worked hard to get everything out that I could. Over the next thirteen days, I made eleven trips to the ship. I collected many useful things, including nails, hatchets, cable, a grindstone, clothing, the canvas sails, a hammock, bedding, silverware, some sheets of iron, and more food and weaponry. Then there was another long, powerful storm. When it had passed, the ship was gone. I was sad, but I knew that I hadn't wasted any time and that I had, in fact, gotten nearly everything of value onto shore.

Well, the next order of business was to find myself a place to live that would offer shelter from the sun, rain, and animals. It also had to be close to fresh water and offer a view of the sea in case a ship sailed close by. After searching for most of a day, I found a plain on the side of a rising hill that suited my needs. There was a wall of thick black rock with a sort of hollowed-out part at the back of the plain. I pitched my tent in front of this hollow and then built a strong, secure fence to protect myself and my belongings.

55

Commas

Add commas where they belong in the sentences below.
Ask the cook, the lady in the white hat, for the recipe.
I wanted to knit a hat, so I bought some yarn.
There were two apples but only one banana.
My dog, a golden retriever, loves to play outside.
I was very tired, for it was after midnight.
She is going to take a bath and then a nap.

56

Edit this passage from *Robinson Crusoe* by adding commas where they belong.

There are 12 errors in this passage.

It took much sweat and hard work to complete my home. Over the first several months, I hollowed out a larger portion of the rock to make more room for myself and my belongings. I built a table, a chair, and some shelves. I also continued to strengthen my roof and fence.

During my first year on the island, I looked for food regularly. There were a number of goats on the island, as well as birds and fish. I had thrown out some chicken feed in order to use the bag. A few weeks later, much to my surprise, I found corn and rice growing. It would be years before I could spare any for food, but I was careful to gather the seed and sow it again in the proper season.

I also explored more of the island. I built a smaller home, a tree fort, in a pleasant valley filled with fruit trees.

I kept track of the days by cutting notches in a post. When it had been one whole year, I remembered the day by fasting and setting it apart as a religious exercise. I confessed my sins, prayed, and praised God.

Semi-Colons

Add commas and semi-colons where they belong in the sentences below.

The phone rang; it was my aunt.

Macy likes to draw, but she doesn't have much time.

I bought four cartons of yogurt; now there are only three.

We liked that roller coaster; it was exciting.

Robert can come inside or stay in the car.

I ordered water to quench my thirst; a burger, french fries, and cole slaw for my meal; and a chocolate milkshake for dessert.

Edit this passage from *Robinson Crusoe* by adding commas and semi-colons where they belong.

There are 13 errors in this passage.

Over the next several years, I kept myself busy with many different tasks. I went hunting and fishing; I made baskets, candles, dishes, and clothes; and I cleared land for farming. I planted my corn and rice each year until I finally had enough to spare some for eating. Then I had to figure out how to grind it up and bake it into bread. These things would have been simple with the proper tools and knowledge, but in my case they took a very long time.

I also explored the whole of the island. I captured a parrot and taught it to speak, found turtles to add to my diet, and succeeded in taming a goat. I continued to harvest fruit and dry grapes, for I enjoyed having raisins with my bread when it was too wet to go out and hunt.

After eleven years on the island, I decided to capture some goats and tame them so that I wouldn't have to hunt. I built a pen and captured a few young goats; within three and a half years I had a nice flock. Now I had a good supply of meat and milk, and after many attempts I was also able to make butter and cheese.

Review Time!

Edit this passage from *Robinson Crusoe* by adding commas and semi-colons where they belong.

There are 9 errors in this passage.

In my fifteenth year on the island, I made a startling discovery. I found a man's footprint in the sand; it was much too big to be my own. I was so shaken that I ran to my fortress and didn't come out for three days. My mind raced with wild thoughts, and I pondered what I should do. I had planted trees so thick around my fence that it was completely hidden, but I planted more to add extra security.

I lived in fear for two years without seeing any other sign of human life. Then one day I came upon the remains of a bonfire. I could see that these were cannibals who had come from one of the smaller islands. After making this unsettling discovery, I stayed close to my home for two more years.

Some years later I saw five large canoes land on my shore. They were filled with cannibals. One of their prisoners tried to escape. Three of the cannibals chased him, but I scared them away with my weapons. The prisoner was very surprised to see me but very grateful for my help. I named him Friday; this was the day I had saved him. Friday, the escaped prisoner, came to live with me.

Quotes

Emphasize that there are quotation marks on either side of the quote and that the speaker's name and any "said" words (said, replied, asked, told, answered, etc.) do not go inside the quotation marks.

Please note that when students are editing, missing quotation marks count as only one error although students will always add them in pairs.

Add quotation marks where they belong in the sentences below.
Monica asked, "Where do the stars hide during the day?"
My neighbor told me he was going on vacation.
"I don't like storms," the little girl stated. "They are very scary!"
Callie said that she doesn't like peas.
"I made apple pie," Mom said. "It will be ready in an hour."
"Here is your newspaper," the boy said.
My uncle replied, "You're welcome."

Edit this passage from *Robinson Crusoe*.

There are 12 errors in this passage.

As Friday was himself a cannibal, I was very careful at first. However, I soon found that I had nothing to worry about. Although he couldn't speak English, he took great care to let (I / me) know that he was my servant. I soon learned to trust Friday; he became my faithful companion. I taught him English and showed him all that I had accomplished on the island. I fed him goat and made him understand that he was never to eat a human again. I also taught him how to use a gun, which he was very scared of at first. Friday and I lived together for three years. These were the happiest years I spent on the island.

In my twenty-seventh year on the island, the cannibals came back again. Friday and I were able to rescue two of their prisoners. One of them was a Spaniard, and the other one was Friday's father! Both of the men were thankful for our help and willingly placed themselves under my leadership.

"Now that you (is / are) here, Father," Friday said, "I am truly content."

Quotes

Add capital letters and punctuation to the sentences below.
"Look at that alligator," Bruce said. "It has sharp teeth."
"Why are we whispering?" I whispered.
"Run!" my sister yelled.
"My favorite tree," Mom said, "is the mighty oak."
Shannon said, "This is my house."
The boy said that he wasn't hungry.

Edit this passage from *Robinson Crusoe*.

There are 13 errors in this passage.

Several months later I saw an English ship. Since there hadn't been any storms, I was suspicious that these men were up to no good. Eleven of the men came on shore in a boat, and three of them were bound. These three were left under a tree while the others left to explore the island.

"Come along, Friday," I ordered. "We are going to investigate."

We armed ourselves and went to speak with the bound men. One of them was the captain of the ship, one was his mate, and the other was a passenger.

The captain explained, "The rest of the soldiers have mutinied. They are going to leave us here and take the ship!"

I freed the three men after they had pledged their loyalty to me. The captain and I came up with a plan to take his ship back. We attacked the men who had betrayed the captain and spared those the captain knew were good men. We left the leaders of the mutiny on the island; the rest of us set sail. After twenty-eight years on the island, I was finally on my way home!

Review Time!

Edit this passage from *Little Women*.

There are 15 errors in this passage.

"It isn't going to feel like Christmas without any presents," Jo complained.

"I hate being poor!" Meg joined in.

"It's not fair that some girls have nothing," added Amy, "while other girls have lots of pretty things."

"We have our family and lots of love," Beth said softly.

The other three girls cheered up a little, but they were all thinking the same thing. Father was away at the war, and it didn't feel like (they / them) had their family for Christmas.

The March sisters were gathered around the fire. Meg, the oldest, was sixteen. She was very pretty, with large eyes, brown hair, and soft white hands. Jo was fifteen years old; she was nothing like her older sister. She was tall and thin, and her only true beauty was her long hair. She was not very ladylike, which often horrified her sisters. Thirteen-year-old Beth was very shy and timid, and she was well-loved by everyone. The youngest, Amy, was twelve. She had blue eyes and golden hair and always tried her best to be a lady.

Homophones

Circle the correct words in the sentences below.

(To / Too / Two) of my sisters have birthdays in April.

That is (are / our) house. (It's / Its) very old. It's older (than / then) me.

The sky is very (blew / blue) today. (There / Their) are no clouds.

Have you ever (read / red) *Cinderella*? (It's / Its) a good story.

(Hear / Here) is the birds' nest. I can (hear / here) them chirping.

Lindsey likes (to / too / two) play tag. Jane likes to play (to / too / two).

The frog (ate / eight) the bug. (Than / Then) he jumped in the water.

This is my dresser. (It's / Its) drawers are very large.

Edit this passage from *Little Women*.

There are 11 errors in this passage.

When Mrs. March came home, the girls gathered around to (hear / here) her read a letter from Mr. March. Afterwards, the girls felt guilty for (there / their) selfish thoughts earlier in the day. Mrs. March, in her loving, motherly way, reminded the girls of how they used (to / two) play Pilgrim's Progress. She told them to play it in real life and see how far they could get before their father came home.

The girls were very pleased with the idea, and they each shared their burden. Meg's burden was that she was too proud of her looks and didn't like to work.

Jo said, "My burden is being (to / too) rough and wild and always wishing I was somewhere more exciting."

Amy thought that her burden was being too selfish.

Nobody thought that good-natured Beth would have a burden. However, Beth shared that her burden was envying girls with nice pianos, being more timid (then / than) usual, and not enjoying her housework.

The March girls were determined to rid themselves of their burdens by the time their father came home.

Edit this passage from *Little Women*.

There are 10 errors in this passage.

On Christmas morning each of the girls received a beautiful Bible from their mother. The girls treasured (their / they're) precious books and decided to read them every day.

The girls had a surprise for Mother as well. Instead of buying presents for themselves, the girls decided to buy gifts for their mother. They bought her new gloves, slippers, handkerchiefs, and a little bottle of perfume.

When the girls went down for breakfast, their mother had just come in from visiting a poor family. (She / He) asked the girls if they would give their Christmas breakfast away, and the girls agreed. They packed everything up and took it to the hungry Hummel family, who thought the girls were Christmas angels.

The (for / four) sisters were rewarded (for / four) their kindness that evening. Mr. Laurence, their rich neighbor, heard about their sacrifice. He sent over all kinds of delicious treats as well as some beautiful flowers. How wonderful their Christmas turned out to be after all!

Edit this passage from *Little Women*.

There are 8 errors in this passage.

   Mr. Laurence had a fifteen-year-old grandson who lived with him.
His name was Theodore, but he preferred to be called Laurie. Jo
had met Laurie once, and she had discovered that (he / him) was
very lonely. Although he lived with his grandfather and many
servants in a large house, he didn't have very many friends.
   Jo went over to the big house one day after Mr. Laurence had left.
She threw a snowball at Laurie's window. He smiled and opened
the window. Laurie had a cold and hadn't been out for a while. He
asked Jo (to / too) come and keep him company. Mrs. March
agreed to let Jo go inside.
   When Jo stepped inside of the big house, she was awed by all
of the beautiful things. She had brought a basket of presents from
her family, and Laurie was very happy. He told Jo that he often
watched her family and was jealous of their love and happiness.
The two became fast friends. Laurie was excited to meet the rest
of the March family.
   From that day on the Laurences and the Marches (was / were)
very good friends. Laurie spent much of his time with the girls, who
loved Laurie like a brother.

Edit this passage from *Little Women*.

There are 12 errors in this passage.

   Although all of the girls were now free to go to Laurie's house as
often as they wished, it took Beth a long time to get over her
shyness. Mr. Laurence owned a beautiful piano; he knew that Beth
would love to play it. He was very kind, and he came to tell her
that she could come over anytime and would not be bothered. Beth
was so grateful for this wonderful gift that she decided to knit Mr.
Laurence a pair of slippers. Beth worked very hard on the slippers,
and she was well-rewarded. Dear Mr. Laurence sent her a lovely
thank-you note and a beautiful little piano!
   While Beth was overcoming her shyness, Amy had a trial of her
own. She was often teased by the richer girls at school. One day
she brought limes to pass out to her friends. Mr. Davis, the teacher,
had outlawed limes, but Amy didn't care. Her friends had given her
many limes, and Amy wanted to prove that she could afford the
treats (to / too).   When Mr. Davis caught Amy, he struck her hand
and made her stand in front of the class until recess. Poor Amy's
pride had caused her deep humiliation!

Confusing Words

Circle the correct words in the sentences below.
That was a very (good / well) meal. (Can / May) I be excused?
She is going to (lie / lay) down. She has (a / an) headache.
I (can / may) bake cupcakes. I bake very (good / well).
There is (a / an) ostrich. It has (a / an) large egg.
This is a really (good / well) book. It ended (good / well).
(Can / May) we go to the beach? I will bring (a / an) picnic lunch.
Please (lie / lay) the newspaper on the table.

Edit this passage from *Little Women*.

There are 9 errors in this passage.

   Jo's character was also tested. She and Amy had (a / an) fight,
and Jo said she would never forgive Amy. One day Jo went ice
skating with Laurie. Amy followed them, but Jo refused to wait for
her younger sister. As a result of Jo's impatience, Amy was (to /
too) far away to (here / hear) that the ice was thin in the middle.
She [fell] into the cold water below. Jo and Laurie rescued her; Jo
begged for forgiveness. The (to / two) sisters were friends again!
   Meg did not escape without learning a lesson of her own. When
Meg was invited for a stay with her friend, Annie Moffat, she was
very excited. Annie Moffat was very rich and dressed very (good /
well). Meg couldn't help comparing her old [dresses] to Annie's
new ones. One night Meg let the other girls dress her up for a
party. They fixed her hair, loaned her a dress, and made her look
like a doll. Meg enjoyed all of the pretty things until she saw
Laurie, who disapproved of her outfit. Meg was ashamed that she
had let her pride take over her (good / well) sense.

Edit this passage from *Little Women*.

There are 7 errors in this passage.

One day Laurie saw the March sisters walking out of their house. The four girls stopped in a shady clearing and began to work. Meg was sewing, Amy was sketching, and Jo was knitting and reading out loud. Beth was gathering pinecones for decorations. Laurie asked if (he / him) could join them, and Meg said that he was welcome as long as he wasn't idle. This was one of the ways the girls played Pilgrim's Progress. When they had nothing else to do, they came to the clearing to enjoy the outdoors but still keep busy.

As the group enjoyed their work, they began to talk about their dreams. Laurie said that his was to travel and become a famous musician. Meg wanted to be the mistress of a lovely house filled with beautiful things. Jo wanted a stable full of horses and (a / an) inkstand that was magic to help her write wonderful stories. Now that Beth had her wonderful piano, she wanted nothing more than to stay at home with Mother and Father. Amy wanted to go to Rome and become the [best] artist in the world.

73

Edit this passage from *Little Women*.

There are 9 errors in this passage.

Jo spent much of her time busily writing by herself, trying to perfect her [stories].

One day she [threw] her pen down with a sigh and exclaimed, "This is the best I can do! If (its / it's) not (good / well) enough, I'll just have to wait!"

Jo packed up her papers and quietly left the house. She walked to a building in town, where she stayed for less (then / than) ten minutes.

For the next two weeks, Jo's sisters thought she acted very strangely. It was plain to see she had a secret, but no one knew what it was. One day Jo came inside with a newspaper. She read a story out loud to her sisters. They all enjoyed it, and Beth asked who had written it. Jo showed them the paper. Her name was printed underneath the story! Her dreams (was / were) starting to come true!

74

Edit this passage from *Little Women*.

There are 12 errors in this passage.

One dreary day in November, the March family received a telegram. Mrs. March read it and dropped onto her chair. Jo took the telegram and read (it / them) to the others. It said that (they're / their) father was very sick! Mrs. March made plans to take the train to see him the very next morning, and the girls [flew] about helping her get ready.

Mrs. March did not have the money for the long journey. She would have to borrow it from old Aunt March. Jo, feeling helpless, suddenly ran out of the house. When she came back, she handed her mother twenty-five dollars.

"Where did you get this?" Mrs. March asked.

Jo pulled off her bonnet, and the family gasped at her short, curly hair. Jo had sold her long brown locks!

Mrs. March was very grateful. She left early the next morning, telling the girls to hope and keep busy.

75

Prefixes and Suffixes

Try to guess the meanings of the following prefixes and suffixes.

I was unhappy because the decision was unjust. _____ not _____

The tricycle had a triangular seat. _____ three _____

My mother was thankful that I was so helpful. _____ full of _____

Dennis waved and called out a friendly greeting. _____ past tense _____

76

109

Edit this passage from *Little Women*.

There are 9 errors in this passage.

For the first week their mother was gone, the March girls behaved very (good / well). However, they soon slipped back into more carefree ways. Only Beth remembered her mother's instructions. She faithfully visited the poor Hummels every day. One day B̲eth came home crying, and Jo went to comfort her. Beth had just come back from the H̲ummel's house. The baby had been sick, and it had died on Betẖ's lap while Mrs̱. Hummel was getting the doctor. W̲hen the doctor had arrived, he said it had died of scarlet fever. Meg and Jo had already had scarlet feveṟ, but Amy and Beth had not.

Beth did get the fever, and Amy was sent away to live with A̲unt March until Beth was better. Beth was very sick for many days, sicker (then / than) her sisters ever knew. Meg and Jo were relieved when their mother came home. They had done their best to nurse Beth, but (they / them) were very weary of the heavy burden. Just when it seemed that Beth could get no worse̱, she [began] to get better. She was finally able to sit on the couch and play with her kittens or sew again.

77

Edit this passage from *Little Women*.

There are 10 errors in this passage.

Although Beth never really got her strength back, she was soon more like her old self. Amy returned home̱, and the household (was / were) cheerful once again. Mr. March was also doing much betteṟ; he wrote that he would be able to come home soon.

During these peaceful weeks, C̲hristmas came again. The girls enjoyed their thoughtful gifts from each otheṟ, Mrs. Marcẖ, and old Mr. Laurence. Just when the girls decided they couldṉ't hold any more happiness, Laurie burst in the door with another surprise. Mr. March walked in behind him, and the girls began laughing and crying. Everyone gathered close by while M̲r. M̲arch told the story of his travels.

The happy family sat down to Christmas dinner. Mr. March could see the differences in his little women after their dedication to Pilgrim's Progress. He [spoke] to his daughters kindly, complimenting each one on her improved virtues. Despite their lack of money, the March family felt very rich indeeḏ!

78

Edit this passage from *The Call of the Wild*.

There are 11 errors in this passage.

Buck was four years old when man struck gold in the Klondike. Because Buck was a dog̱, he was unaware that this event would greatly change his life. Buck had lived his whole life at J̲udge M̲iller's place in Santa Clara Valley, C̲alifornia. Judge Miller owned a big house with a large porch. Behind the house were stables̱, servants' cottages̱, pastures̱, and orchards. This was the wondrous home over which Buck ruled.

He went swimming and hunting with Judge Miller's sons, and he accompanied Judge Milleṟ's daughters on their frequent walks. On cold nights Buck enjoyed resting at Judge Miller's feet by the warm fire.

Buck's father was a St. Bernard, and his mother was a Scotch shepherd dog. Buck was not as big as his fatheṟ, but he was nevertheless a handsome dog of 140 pounds. Although B̲uck enjoyed an easy life, his love of hunting and other outdoor activities had shaped his muscles and kept him from being a spoiled house dog.

79

Edit this passage from *The Call of the Wild*.

There are 9 errors in this passage.

As Buck continued to enjoy his (good / well) life at Judge Miller's house, (their / there) were two things he did not know. The first was the gold strike in the Klondike. The second was that Manueḻ, one of the gardeners̱, was not someone Buck should have trusted.

Manuel was very good at wasting his money. Instead of using his money to take care of his family̱, he gambled it away.

One night M̲anuel took Buck for a walk. Only one other person saw them, and that person gave Manuel some money. Manuel put a rope around Bucḵ's neck and handed the rope to the stranger. Buck had learned to trust meṉ, but he didṉ't trust the stranger. He growled at the man, who pulled the rope tighter. Buck was shockeḏ! He had never been treated harshly before.

Buck was loaded on a train and passed from stranger to stranger. Several days later Buck arrived in S̲eattle caged in a crate.

80

Expressive Words

Rewrite the sentences using expressive nouns, verbs, adverbs, and adjectives. Answers will vary.

The girl ran across the street.

The little girl dashed quickly across Main Street.

We had a party for Tracy.

We threw a surprise birthday party for our cousin, Tracy.

He drew a picture.

He slowly sketched a small cartoon.

I had a glass of water.

I drank a large glass of cool, refreshing water.

81

Edit this passage from _The Call of the Wild_.

There are 8 errors in this passage.

In Seattle Buck learned another harsh lesson. He learned that he must obey a man with a weapon. During Buck's time here, he saw many other dogs come and go. Men would come and give the man in charge money, and (then / than) they would take some dogs. Buck wondered where the dogs went, and he [knew] one day he would find out.

Sure enough, one day a man named Perrault gave the man some money and took Buck and Curly, a Newfoundland, away with him. They joined another man named Francois. Buck soon learned that Perrault and Francois worked for the Canadian government. They were fair [men], and Buck learned to respect them.

Perrault and Francois also had two other dogs. The first dog, Dave, took no interest in anything and seemed almost bored. The other dog, Spitz, seemed friendly, but he was sneaky and cared only about himself. He often tried to steal food from the other dogs.

82

Edit this passage from _The Call of the Wild_.

There are 10 errors in this passage.

When Buck and his new owners landed in Dyea, Alaska, Buck saw snow for the very first time. At first it startled him, and Francois and Perrault laughed at him. However, the snow was not the only new thing there.

Buck soon learned the rules of wild dogs. Here the dogs were not friends; every dog had to take care of himself. Although in his old life Buck never would have stolen, here he learned to steal food from his owners and from the other dogs.

Francois and Perrault [bought] several more dogs. Soon they were ready to get to work. As couriers for the Canadian government, the men were in charge of delivering important dispatches. They needed a team of strong, hardy dogs to pull their sled many miles through the cold and snow.

Although Buck had never worked as a sled dog, he learned very quickly. Spitz was a (good / well) lead dog, but Francois and Perrault were even more impressed by Buck.

83

Edit this passage from _The Call of the Wild_.

There are 11 errors in this passage.

As Buck and the team [ran] day after day, Buck grew used to the work. His muscles strengthened, his feet hardened, and he learned to live in the cold weather. The dogs were pushed very hard; they were exhausted by the end of each day.

One day Spitz attacked Buck. Spitz, always a bully, was jealous of the attention Buck received. Francois separated Buck from Spitz, but from that moment on they were [enemies]. At the end of another long day, Spitz stole Buck's sleeping spot.

As the leader of the team, Spitz (was / were) responsible for keeping the other dogs in line. Buck began to rebel, and he encouraged the other dogs to cause trouble as well.

Finally the time came. Spitz stole a rabbit that Buck had chased down, and Buck refused to walk away. This time the dogs were going to fight it out, and only the winner would come back.

84

111

Edit this passage from *The Call of the Wild*.

There are 8 errors in this passage.

The next morning Ḟrancois and Ṗerrault were surprised to see that Spitz was gone. They chose a new dog to be the leader, but Buck would not let them harness the new dog up. Instead, Buck insisted on being the lead dog. He felt like he had earned it. Finally Francois and Perrault [gave] in and made Buck the new leader.

Buck wasted no time. He made the other dogs pull and run as fast as (they / them) could. With Buck in the lead, Francois and Perrault made record time.

Official orders forced Francois and Perrault to sell the dogs, which made the men very unhappy. Now the dogs pulled a heavy load of mail for some other men. Even though the team was making good time, (there / their / they're) was so much mail that the dogs weren't able to get enough rest between runs. Eventually these men (to / too) were ordered to sell the tired dogs.

Ḃuck and the rest of the exhausted team (was / were) bought for a very low price by an inexperienced family joining the search for gold.

85

Sentence Combining

If students need help with sentence combining, ask them questions like this: "What information in each sentence is new information that needs to be included, and what information is repeated and unnecessary?" "How can you fit the new information into the old sentence?" Once they can identify the new information in each sentence, they can combine those parts to form one complete sentence.

Combine each group of sentences below into one sentence. **Answers will vary.**

I'm going to the potluck. I'm taking lasagna. I'm also taking a salad.
I'm taking lasagna and a salad to the potluck.

I bought a card for my mom. It was a Mother's Day card. The card was pink and white.
I bought a pink and white Mother's Day card for my mom.

Our dog had puppies. They are cute. There are five of them.
Out dog had five cute puppies.

Arthur is good at math. He is good at science. He likes spelling the most.
Arthur is good at math and science, but he likes spelling the most.

I have to wash the dishes. I also need to dust the shelves. After that I have to sweep the floor.
I have to wash the dishes, dust the shelves, and sweep the floor.

86

Edit this passage from *The Call of the Wild*.

There are 9 errors in this passage.

The team was bought by a man named Ċharles. He was traveling with his wife, Ṁercedes, and his brother-in-law, Ḣal. As soon as Buck walked into his new owners' camp, he knew that he and the other dogs were not going to get the rest they needed. The family was hoping to strike it rich, but they were not prepared for the hard journey. Their camp was a complete mess; they had brought way too many things with them.

Charles, Mercedes, and Hal did not know very much about dogs either. When Buck and his team were unable to pull the overloaded sled, Hal decided that the dogs were just being lazy. He refused to lighten their load, even though many other people warned him that it was (to / too) heavy for the dogs to move.

Finally the family was forced to leave some of their belongings behind and buy more dogs.

87

Edit this passage from *The Call of the Wild*.

There are 8 errors in this passage.

Even with a lighter sled and more dogs, life was hard for Ḃuck and his team. They had still not gotten the chance to rest after their long mail days, and their new owners did not know how to care for them properly.

Life on the trail was much harder than Ċharles and his family had anticipated. They did not adapt very well. They were not able to cover as many miles each day as they had planned, and the family began to run out of supplies. The dogs were given less food each day, but (they / them) were still expected to work just as hard.

Other people along the long, dangerous trail often tried to give Charles and Hal advice, but they were too proud to listen.

One day Buck could not get up. Despite a beating from Hal, he was unable to move. A man named Ṙohn Ṫhornton stopped Hal and rescued Buck. As Charles and Hal and the other dogs disappeared from sight, John knelt next to Buck and [spoke] to him kindly. Buck was going to get the rest he needed at last.

88

112